MW00633829

# Plants and Animals

## FOSS

**FULL
OPTION
SCIENCE
SYSTEM**

**3rd Edition**

Developed at the Lawrence Hall of Science, University of California, Berkeley
Published and Distributed by Delta Education

**FOSS Lawrence Hall of Science Team**

Larry Malone and Linda De Lucchi, FOSS Project Codirectors and Lead Developers

Kathy Long, FOSS Assessment Director; David Lippman, Project Specialist and Editor; Carol Sevilla, Publications Design Coordinator; Rose Craig, Illustrator; Susan Stanley, Graphic Production; John Quick, Photographer; Trudihope Schlomowitz, Barbara Clinton, Editors; DeSondra Ward, Office Manager

**FOSS Curriculum Developers:** Brian Campbell, Teri Dannenberg, Alan Gould, Susan Kaschner Jagoda, Ann Moriarty, Jessica Penchos, Kimi Hosoume, Virginia Reid, Terry Shaw, Joanna Snyder, Erica Beck Spencer, Diana Velez, Natalie Yakushij

**FOSS Technology Developers:** Susan Ketchner, Habiba Noor, Arzu Orgad

**FOSS Multimedia Team:** Kate Jordan, Multimedia Director; Nicole Medina, Senior Multimedia Producer; Matthew Jacoby, Lead Programmer; Geoffrey Thomas, Multimedia Programmer and Designer; Chris Linden, Designer; Chris Hamamoto, Designer; Dan Bluestein, Programmer; Roger Vang, Programmer; Christopher Cianciarulo, Programmer

**Delta Education Team**

Bonnie A. Piotrowski, FOSS Editorial Director

**Project Team:** Mathew Bacon, Jennifer Apt, Sandra Burke, Tom Guetling, Joann Hoy, Jacquelyn Lachance, Lisa Lachance, Paulette Miley, John Prescott, Stella Rozzi

**Thank you to all FOSS Grades K-6 Trial Teachers**

Heather Ballard, Wilson Elementary, Coppell, TX; Mirith Ballestas De Barroso, Treasure Forest Elementary, Houston, TX; Terra L. Barton, Harry McKillop Elementary, Melissa, TX; Rhonda Bernard, Frances E. Norton Elementary, Allen, TX; Theresa Bissonnette, East Millbrook Magnet Middle School, Raleigh, NC; Peter Blackstone, Hall Elementary School, Portland, ME; Tiffani Brisco, Seven Hills Elementary, Newark, TX; Darrow Brown, Lake Myra Elementary School, Wendell, NC; Heather Callaghan, Olive Chapel Elementary, Apex, NC; Katie Cannon, Las Colinas Elementary, Irving, TX; Elaine M. Cansler, Brassfield Road Elementary School, Raleigh, NC; Kristy Cash, Wilson Elementary, Coppell, TX; Monica Coles, Swift Creek Elementary School, Raleigh, NC; Shirley Conner, Ocean Avenue Elementary School, Portland, ME; Sally Connolly, Cape Elizabeth Middle School, Cape Elizabeth, ME; Melissa Cook-Airhart, Harry McKillop Elementary, Melissa, TX; Melissa Costa, Olive Chapel Elementary, Apex, NC; Hillary P. Croissant, Harry McKillop Elementary, Melissa, TX; Rene Custeau, Hall Elementary School, Portland, ME; Nancy Davis, Martha and Josh Morriss Mathematics and Engineering Elementary School, Texarkana, TX; Nancy Deveneau, Wilson Elementary, Coppell, TX; Karen Diaz, Las Colinas Elementary, Irving, TX; Marlana Dumas, Las Colinas Elementary, Irving, TX; Mary Evans, R.E. Good Elementary School, Carrollton, TX; Jacquelyn Farley, Moss Haven Elementary, Dallas, TX; Corinna Ferrier, Oak Forest Elementary, Humble, TX; Allison Fike, Wilson Elementary, Coppell, TX; Barbara Fugitt, Martha and Josh Morriss Mathematics and Engineering Elementary School, Texarkana, TX; Colleen Garvey, Farmington Woods Elementary, Cary, NC; Judy Geller, Bentley Elementary School, Oakland, CA; Erin Gibson, Las Colinas Elementary, Irving, TX; Kelli Gobel, Melissa Ridge Intermediate School, Melissa, TX; Dollie Green, Melissa Ridge Intermediate School, Melissa, TX; Brenda Lee Harrigan, Bentley Elementary School, Oakland, CA; Cori Harris, Samuel Beck Elementary, Trophy Club, TX; Kim Hayes, Martha and Josh Morriss Mathematics and Engineering Elementary School, Texarkana, TX; Staci Lynn Hester, Lacy Elementary School, Raleigh, NC; Amanda Hill, Las Colinas Elementary, Irving, TX; Margaret Hillman, Ocean Avenue Elementary School, Portland, ME; Cindy Holder, Oak Forest Elementary, Humble, TX; Sarah Huber, Hodge Road Elementary, Knightdale, NC; Susan Jacobs, Granger Elementary, Keller, TX; Carol Kellum, Wallace Elementary, Dallas, TX; Jennifer A. Kelly, Hall Elementary School, Portland, ME; Brittani Kern, Fox Road Elementary, Raleigh, NC; Jodi Lay, Lufkin Road Middle School, Apex, NC; Melissa Lourenco, Lake Myra Elementary School, Wendell, NC; Ana Martinez, RISD Academy, Dallas, TX; Shaheen Mavani, Las Colinas Elementary, Irving, TX; Mary Linley McClendon, Math Science Technology Magnet School, Richardson, TX; Adam McKay, Davis Drive Elementary, Cary, NC; Leslie Meadows, Lake Myra Elementary School, Wendell, NC; Anne Mechler, J. Erik Jonsson Community School, Dallas, TX; Anne Miller, J. Erik Jonsson Community School, Dallas, TX; Shirley Diann Miller, The Rice School, Houston, TX; Keri Minier, Las Colinas Elementary, Irving, TX; Stephanie Renee Nance, T.H. Rogers Elementary, Houston, TX; Cynthia Nilsen, Peaks Island School, Peaks Island, ME; Elizabeth Noble, Las Colinas Elementary, Irving, TX; Courtney Noonan, Shadow Oaks Elementary School, Houston, TX; Sarah Peden, Aversboro Elementary School, Garner, NC; Carrie Prince, School at St. George Place, Houston, TX; Marlaina Pritchard, Melissa Ridge Intermediate School, Melissa, TX; Alice Pujol, J. Erik Jonsson Community School, Dallas, TX; Claire Ramsbotham, Cape Elizabeth Middle School, Cape Elizabeth, ME; Paul Rendon, Bentley Elementary, Oakland, CA; Janette Ridley, W.H. Wilson Elementary School, Coppell, TX; Kristina (Crickett) Roberts, W.H. Wilson Elementary School, Coppell, TX; Heather Rogers, Wendell Creative Arts & Science Magnet Elementary School, Wendell, NC; Alissa Royal, Melissa Ridge Intermediate School, Melissa, TX; Megan Runion, Olive Chapel Elementary, Apex, NC; Christy Scheef, J. Erik Jonsson Community School, Dallas, TX; Samrawit Shawl, T.H. Rogers School, Houston, TX; Nicole Spivey, Lake Myra Elementary School, Wendell, NC; Ashley Stephenson, J. Erik Jonsson Community School, Dallas, TX; Jolanta Stern, Browning Elementary School, Houston, TX; Gale Stimson, Bentley Elementary, Oakland, CA; Ted Stoeckley, Hall Middle School, Larkspur, CA; Cathryn Sutton, Wilson Elementary, Coppell, TX; Camille Swander, Ocean Avenue Elementary School, Portland, ME; Brandi Swann, Westlawn Elementary School, Texarkana, TX; Robin Taylor, Arapaho Classical Magnet, Richardson, TX; Michael C. Thomas, Forest Lane Academy, Dallas, TX; Jomarga Thompkins, Lockhart Elementary, Houston, TX; Mary Timar, Madera Elementary, Lake Forest, CA; Helena Tongkeamha, White Rock Elementary, Dallas, TX; Linda Trampe, J. Erik Jonsson Community School, Dallas, TX; Charity VanHorn, Fred A. Olds Elementary, Raleigh, NC; Kathleen VanKeuren, Lufkin Road Middle School, Apex, NC; Valerie Vassar, Hall Elementary School, Portland, ME; Megan Veron, Westwood Elementary School, Houston, TX; Mary Margaret Waters, Frances E. Norton Elementary, Allen, TX; Stephanie Robledo Watson, Ridgecrest Elementary School, Houston, TX; Lisa Webb, Madisonville Intermediate, Madisonville, TX; Matt Whaley, Cape Elizabeth Middle School, Cape Elizabeth, ME; Nancy White, Canyon Creek Elementary, Austin, TX; Barbara Yurick, Oak Forest Elementary, Humble, TX; Linda Zittel, Mira Vista Elementary, Richmond, CA

**Photo Credits:** © iStockphoto/Jeff Goulden (cover); © Zach Smith; © Monkey Business Images/Shutterstock; © David Lippman; © Christian Musat/Shutterstock

**Published and Distributed by Delta Education, a member of the School Specialty Family**

The FOSS program was developed in part with the support of the National Science Foundation grant nos. MDR-8751727 and MDR-9150097. However, any opinions, findings, conclusions, statements, and recommendations expressed herein are those of the authors and do not necessarily reflect the views of NSF. FOSSmap was developed in collaboration between the BEAR Center at UC Berkeley and FOSS at the Lawrence Hall of Science. Score analysis is done through the BEAR Center Scoring Engine.

Plants and Animals — Teacher Toolkit, 1325325
Teacher Resources, 1391947
978-1-60902-698-1
Printing 1 – 10/2012
Webcrafters, Madison, WI

## TABLE OF CONTENTS

# FOSS Introduction

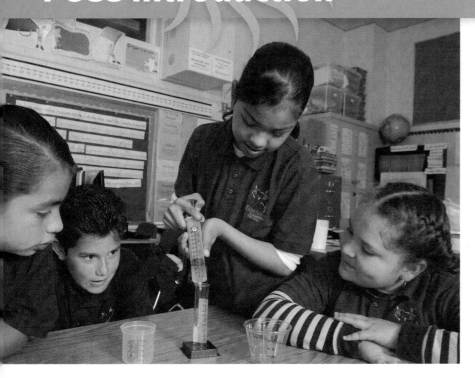

## Contents

# INTRODUCTION

*The Full Option Science System™ has evolved from a philosophy of teaching and learning at the Lawrence Hall of Science that has guided the development of successful active-learning science curricula for more than 40 years. The FOSS Program bridges research and practice by providing tools and strategies to engage students and teachers in enduring experiences that lead to deeper understanding of the natural and designed worlds.*

Science is a creative and analytic enterprise, made active by our human capacity to think. Scientific knowledge advances when scientists observe objects and events, think about how they relate to what is known, test their ideas in logical ways, and generate explanations that integrate the new information into understanding of the natural world. Engineers apply that understanding to solve real-world problems. Thus, the scientific enterprise is both what we know (content knowledge) and how we come to know it (practices). Science is a discovery activity, a process for producing new knowledge.

The best way for students to appreciate the scientific enterprise, learn important scientific and engineering concepts, and develop the ability to think well is to actively participate in scientific practices through their own investigations and analyses. FOSS was created to engage students and teachers with meaningful experiences in the natural and designed worlds.

## GOALS OF THE FOSS PROGRAM

FOSS has set out to achieve three important goals: scientific literacy, instructional efficiency, and systemic reform.

### Scientific Literacy

FOSS provides all students with science experiences that are appropriate to students' cognitive development and prior experiences. It provides a foundation for more advanced understanding of core science ideas which are organized in thoughtfully designed learning progressions and prepares students for life in an increasingly complex scientific and technological world.

The National Research Council (NRC) in *A Framework for K–12 Science Education* and the American Association for the Advancement of Science (AAAS) in *Benchmarks for Scientific Literacy,* have described the characteristics of scientific literacy:

- Familiarity with the natural world, its diversity, and its interdependence.

- Understanding the disciplinary core ideas and the crosscutting concepts of science, such as patterns; cause and effect; scale, proportion, and quantity; systems and system models; energy and matter—flows, cycles, and conservation; structure and function; and stability and change.

- Knowing that science and engineering, technology, and mathematics are interdependent human enterprises and, as such, have implied strengths and limitations.

- Ability to reason scientifically.

- Using scientific knowledge and scientific and engineering practices for personal and social purposes.

The FOSS Program design is based on learning progressions that provide students with opportunities to investigate core ideas in science in increasingly complex ways over time. FOSS starts with the intuitive ideas that primary students bring with them and provides experiences that allow students to develop more sophisticated understanding as they grow through the grades. Cognitive research tells us that learning involves individuals in actively constructing schemata to organize new information and to relate and incorporate the new understanding into established knowledge. What sets experts apart from novices is that experts in a discipline have extensive knowledge that is effectively organized into structured schemata to promote thinking. Novices have disconnected ideas about a topic that are difficult to retrieve and use. Through internal processes to establish schemata and through social processes of interacting with peers and adults, students construct understanding of the natural world and their relationship to it. The target goal for FOSS students is to know and use scientific explanations of the natural world and the designed world; to understand the nature and development of scientific knowledge and technological capabilities; and to participate productively in scientific and engineering practices.

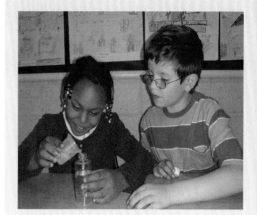

## Instructional Efficiency

FOSS provides all teachers with a complete, cohesive, flexible, easy-to-use science program that reflects current research on teaching and learning, including student discourse, argumentation, writing to learn, and reflective thinking, as well as teacher use of formative assessment to guide instruction. The FOSS Program uses effective instructional methodologies, including active learning, scientific practices, focus questions to guide inquiry, working in collaborative groups, multisensory strategies, integration of literacy, appropriate use of digital technologies, and making connections to students' lives, including the outdoors.

FOSS is designed to make active learning in science engaging for teachers as well as for students. It includes these supports for teachers:

- Complete equipment kits with durable, well-designed materials for all students.

- Detailed *Investigations Guide* with science background for the teacher and focus questions to guide instructional practice and student thinking.

- Multiple strategies for formative assessment at all grade levels.

- Benchmark assessments (grades 1–6) with online access for administering, coding, and analyzing assessments (grades 3–6).

- Strategies for use of science notebooks for novice and experienced users.

- *FOSS Science Resources,* a book of module-specific readings with strategies for science-centered language development.

- The FOSS website with interactive multimedia activities for use in school or at home, suggested interdisciplinary-extension activities, and extensive online support for teachers, including teacher prep videos.

## Systemic Reform

FOSS provides schools and school systems with a program that addresses the community science-achievement standards. The FOSS Program prepares students by helping them acquire the knowledge and thinking capacity appropriate for world citizens.

The FOSS Program design makes it appropriate for reform efforts on all scales. It reflects the core ideas to be incorporated into the next-generation science standards. It meets with the approval of science and technology companies working in collaboration with school systems, and it has demonstrated its effectiveness with diverse student and teacher populations in major urban reform efforts. The use of science notebooks and formative-assessment strategies in FOSS redefines the role of science in a school—the way that teachers engage in science teaching with one another as professionals and with students as learners, and the way that students engage in science learning with the teacher and with one another. FOSS takes students and teachers beyond the classroom walls to establish larger communities of learners.

# BRIDGING RESEARCH INTO PRACTICE

The FOSS Program is built on the assumptions that understanding core scientific knowledge and how science functions is essential for citizenship, that all teachers can teach science, and that all students can learn science. The guiding principles of the FOSS design, described below, are derived from research and confirmed through FOSS developers' extensive experience with teachers and students in typical American classrooms.

**Understanding of science develops over time.** FOSS has elaborated learning progressions for core ideas in science for kindergarten through grade 6. Developing the learning progressions involves identifying successively more sophisticated ways of thinking about core ideas over multiple years. "If mastery of a core idea in a science discipline is the ultimate educational destination, then well-designed learning progressions provide a map of the routes that can be taken to reach that destination" (National Research Council, *A Framework for K–12 Science Education*, 2011).

**Focusing on a limited number of topics in science avoids shallow coverage and provides more time to explore core science ideas in depth.** Research emphasizes that fewer topics experienced in greater depth produces much better learning than many topics briefly visited. FOSS affirms this research. FOSS modules provide long-term engagement (9–10 weeks) with important science ideas. Furthermore, modules build upon one another within and across each strand, progressively moving students toward the grand ideas of science. The core ideas of science are difficult and complex, never learned in one lesson or in one class year.

## FOSS Elementary Module Sequences

| | PHYSICAL SCIENCE | | EARTH SCIENCE | | LIFE SCIENCE | |
|---|---|---|---|---|---|---|
| | MATTER | ENERGY AND CHANGE | DYNAMIC ATMOSPHERE | ROCKS AND LANDFORMS | STRUCTURE/ FUNCTION | COMPLEX SYSTEMS |
| 6 | Mixtures and Solutions | Motion, Force, and Models | Weather on Earth | Sun, Moon, and Planets | Living Systems | |
| | Measuring Matter | Energy and Electromagnetism | Water | Soils, Rocks, and Landforms | Structures of Life | Environments |
| | Solids and Liquids | Balance and Motion | Air and Weather | Pebbles, Sand, and Silt | Plants and Animals | Insects and Plants |
| K | Materials in Our World | | Trees and Weather | | Animals Two by Two | |

**Science is more than a body of knowledge.** How well you think is often more important than how much you know. In addition to the science content framework, every FOSS module provides opportunities for students to engage in and understand scientific practices, and many modules explore issues related to engineering practices and the use of natural resources. FOSS promotes these scientific and engineering practices described in *A Framework for K–12 Science Education.*

- Asking questions (for science) and defining problems (for engineering)
- Planning and carrying out investigations
- Analyzing and interpreting data
- Developing and using models
- Using mathematics, information and computer technology, and computational thinking
- Constructing explanations (for science) and designing solutions (for engineering)
- Engaging in argument from evidence
- Obtaining, evaluating, and communicating information

**Science is inherently interesting, and children are natural investigators.** It is widely accepted that children learn science concepts best by doing science. Doing science means hands-on experiences with objects, organisms, and systems. Hands-on activities are motivating for students, and they stimulate inquiry and curiosity. For these reasons, FOSS is committed to providing the best possible materials and the most effective procedures for deeply engaging students with scientific concepts. FOSS students at all grade levels investigate, experiment, gather data, organize results, and draw conclusions based on their own actions. The information gathered in such activities enhances the development of scientific and engineering practices.

**Education is an adventure in self-discovery.** Science provides the opportunity to connect to students' interests and experiences. Prior experiences and individual learning styles are important considerations for developing understanding. Observing is often equated with seeing, but in the FOSS Program all senses are used to promote greater understanding. FOSS evolved from pioneering work done in the 1970s with students with disabilities. The legacy of that work is that FOSS investigations naturally use multisensory methods to accommodate students with physical and learning disabilities and also to maximize information gathering for all students. A number of tools, such as the FOSS syringe and balance, were originally designed to serve the needs of students with disabilities.

**Formative assessment is a powerful tool to promote learning and can change the culture of the learning environment.** Formative assessment in FOSS creates a community of reflective practice. Teachers and students make up the community and establish norms of mutual support, trust, respect, and collaboration. The goal of the community is that everyone will demonstrate progress and will learn and grow.

**Science-centered language development promotes learning in all areas.** Effective use of science notebooks can promote reflective thinking and contribute to life long learning. Research has shown that when language-arts experiences are embedded within the context of learning science, students improve in their ability to use their language skills. Students are eager to read to find out information, and to share their experiences both verbally and in writing.

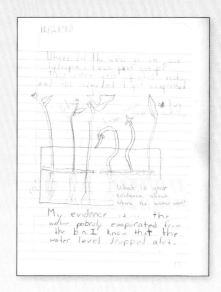

**Experiences out of the classroom develop awareness of community.** By extending classroom learning into the outdoors, FOSS brings the science concepts and principles to life. In the process of validating classroom learning among the schoolyard trees and shrubs, down in the weeds on the asphalt, and in the sky overhead, students will develop a relationship with nature. It is our relationship with natural systems that allows us to care deeply for these systems.

# FOSS COMPONENTS

## *Teacher Toolkit*

The *Teacher Toolkit* is the most important part of the FOSS Program. It is here that all the wisdom and experience contributed by hundreds of educators has been assembled. Everything we know about the content of the module and how to teach the subject is presented, along with the resources that will assist the effort. Each toolkit has three parts.

***Investigations Guide.*** This spiral-bound document contains these chapters.

- Overview
- Materials
- Investigations
- Assessment

***Teacher Resources.*** This collection of resources contains these chapters.

- FOSS Introduction
- Science Notebooks (for Grades K–2 or for Grades 3–6)
- Science-Centered Language Development
- Taking FOSS Outdoors
- FOSSweb and Technology
- Science Notebook Masters (for grades 1–6)
- Teacher Masters
- Assessment Masters

The chapters in *Teacher Resources* and the Spanish duplication masters can also be found on FOSSweb (www.FOSSweb.com) and are available on CDs.

***FOSS Science Resources book.*** This is a copy of the student book of readings that are integrated into the instruction.

## Equipment Kit

The FOSS Program provides the materials needed for the investigations, including metric measuring tools, in sturdy, front-opening drawer-and-sleeve cabinets. Inside, you will find high-quality materials packaged for a class of 32 students. Consumable materials are supplied for two uses.

## FOSS Science Resources Books

*FOSS Science Resources* is a book of original readings developed to accompany each module. The readings are referred to as articles in the *Investigations Guide*. Students read the articles in the book as they progress through the module. The articles cover a specific concept usually after that concept has been introduced in an active investigation. The articles in *FOSS Science Resources* and the discussion questions provided in the *Investigations Guide* help students make connections to the science concepts introduced and explored during the active investigations. Concept development is most effective when students are allowed to experience organisms, objects, and phenomena firsthand before engaging the concepts in text. The text and illustrations help make connections between what students experience concretely and the ideas that explain their observations.

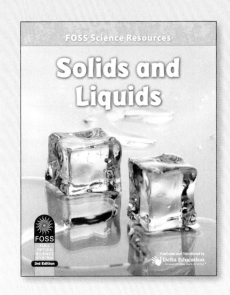

## FOSSweb and Technology

The FOSS website opens new horizons for educators, students, and families, in the classroom or at home. Each module has an interactive site where students and families can find instructional activities, interactive simulations and virtual investigations, and other additional resources. FOSSweb provides resources for professional development, materials management, general teaching tools for FOSS, purchasing links, contact information for the FOSS Program and technical support. You do not need an account to view this general FOSS Program information. In addition to the general information, FOSSweb provides digital access to PDF versions of the *Teacher Resources* component of the *Teacher Toolkit* and digital-only resources that supplement the print and kit materials.

With a FOSSweb educator account, you can set up a customized homepage, which will provide easy access to the digital components of the modules you teach, and allow you to create class pages for your students with access to tutorials and online assessments.

## Ongoing Professional Development

The Lawrence Hall of Science and Delta Education are committed to supporting science educators with unrivaled teacher support, high-quality implementation, and continuous staff-development opportunities and resources. FOSS has a strong network of consultants who have rich and experienced backgrounds in diverse educational settings using FOSS. Find out about professional-development opportunities on FOSSweb.

# FOSS Introduction

## FOSS INSTRUCTIONAL DESIGN

Each FOSS investigation is designed to provide multiple exposures to science concepts. The design includes these pedagogies.

- Active investigation, including outdoor experiences

- Recording in science notebooks to answer the focus question

- Reading in *FOSS Science Resources*

- Assessment to monitor progress and motivate student reflection on learning

In practice, these components are seamlessly integrated into a continuum designed to maximize every student's opportunity to learn. An instructional sequence may move from one pedagogy to another and back again to ensure adequate coverage of a concept.

### Investigation Organization

Modules are subdivided into **investigations** (four in most modules). Investigations are further subdivided into three to five **parts**. Each part of each investigation is driven by a **focus question**. The focus question, usually presented as the part begins, signals the challenge to be met, mystery to be solved, or principle to be uncovered. The focus question guides students' actions and thinking and makes the learning goal of each part explicit for teachers. Each part concludes with students recording an answer to the focus question in their notebooks. Investigation-specific **scientific background** information for the teacher is presented in each investigation chapter. The content discussion is divided into sections, each of which relates directly to one of the focus questions. This section ends with information about teaching and learning and a conceptual-flow diagram for the content.

The **Getting Ready** and **Guiding the Investigation** sections have several features that are flagged or presented in the sidebars. These include several icons to remind you when a particular pedagogical method is suggested, as well as concise bits of information in several categories.

**Teaching notes** appear in blue boxes in the sidebars. These notes comprise a second voice in the curriculum—an educative element. The first (traditional) voice is the message you deliver to students. It supports your work teaching students at all levels, from management to inquiry. The second educative voice, shared as a teaching note, is designed to help you understand the science content and pedagogical rationale at work behind the instructional scene.

## FOCUS QUESTION
*What materials stick to magnets?*

## TEACHING NOTE

*This focus question can be answered with a simple yes or no, but the question has power when students support their answers with evidence. Their answers should take the form Yes, because . . .*

The **safety** icon reminds you of a potential safety issue. It could relate to the use of a chemical substance, such as salt, requiring safety goggles, or the possibility of an allergic reaction when an investigation might expose students to latex, legumes, or wheat.

The small-group **discussion** icon asks you to pause while students discuss data or construct explanations in their groups. Often a Reporter shares the group's conclusions with the class.

The **new-word** icon alerts you to a new vocabulary word or phrase that should be introduced thoughtfully. The new vocabulary should also be entered onto the word wall (or pocket chart). A complete list of the scientific vocabulary used in each investigation appears in the sidebar on the last page of the Background for the Teacher section.

The **vocabulary** icon indicates when students should review recently introduced vocabulary, often just before they will be answering the focus question or preparing for benchmark assessment.

The **recording** icon points out when students should make a science-notebook entry. Students record on prepared notebook sheets or, increasingly, on blank pages in their science notebooks.

The **reading** icon signals when the class should read a specific article in *FOSS Science Resources*, preferably during a reading period.

The **assessment** icon appears when there is an opportunity to assess student progress by using embedded or benchmark assessments. Some of the embedded-assessment methods include observation of students engaged in scientific practices and review of a notebook entry.

The **outdoor** icon signals when to move the science learning experience into the schoolyard. It also helps you plan for selecting and preparing an outdoor site for a student activity.

The **engineering** icon indicates opportunities for addressing engineering practices—applying and using scientific knowledge. These opportunities include developing a solution to a problem, constructing and evaluating models, and using systems thinking.

The **EL Note** in the sidebar provides a specific strategy to assist English learners in developing science concepts. A more fully elaborated discussion of strategies is provided in the Science-Centered Language Development chapter.

### EL NOTE

*See the Science-Centered Language Development chapter for notebook-sharing strategies.*

To help with pacing, you will see the icon for **breakpoints**. Some breakpoints are essential, and others are optional.

## POSSIBLE BREAKPOINT

**Active Investigation**
- *Context*
- *Activity*
- *Data management*
- *Analysis*

## Active Investigation

Active investigation is a master pedagogy. Embedded within active learning are a number of pedagogical elements and practices that keep active investigation vigorous and productive.

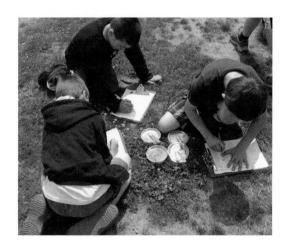

**Context: questioning and planning.** Active investigation requires focus. The context of an inquiry can be established with a focus question or challenge from you or, in some cases, from students. At other times, students are asked to plan a method for investigation. This might start with a teacher demonstration or presentation. Then you challenge students to plan an investigation. In either case, the field available for thought and interaction is constrained. This clarification of context and purpose results in a more productive investigation.

**Activity: doing and observing.** In the practice of science, scientists put things together and take things apart, observe systems and interactions, and conduct experiments. This is the core of science—active, firsthand experience with objects, organisms, materials, and systems in the natural and designed worlds. In FOSS, students engage in the same processes. Students often conduct investigations in collaborative groups of four, with each student taking a role to contribute to the effort.

The active investigations in FOSS are cohesive and build on each other and the readings to lead students to a comprehensive understanding of concepts. Through the investigations, students gather meaningful data.

**Data management: recording and organizing.** Data accrue from observation, both direct (through the senses) and indirect (mediated by instrumentation). Data are the raw material from which scientific knowledge and meaning are synthesized. During and after work with materials, students record data in their notebooks. Data recording is the first of several kinds of student writing.

Students then organize data so that the data will be easier to think about. Tables allow efficient comparison. Organizing data in a sequence (time) or series (physical property) can reveal patterns. Students process some data into graphs, providing visual display of numerical data. Students also organize data and process them in the science notebook.

***Analysis: discussing and writing explanations.*** The most
important part of an active investigation is extracting its meaning. This
constructive process involves logic, discourse, and existing knowledge.
Students share their explanations for phenomena, using evidence
generated during the investigation to support their ideas. They conclude
the active investigation by writing a summary of their learning in their
science notebooks as well as questions raised during the activity.

## Science Notebooks

Research and best practice have led FOSS to place more emphasis
on the student science notebook. Keeping a notebook helps students
organize their observations and data, process their data, and maintain
a record of their learning for future reference. The
process of writing about their science experiences and
communicating their thinking is a powerful learning
device for students. The science-notebook entries
stand as a credible and useful expression of learning.
The artifacts in the notebooks form one of the core
elements of the assessment system.

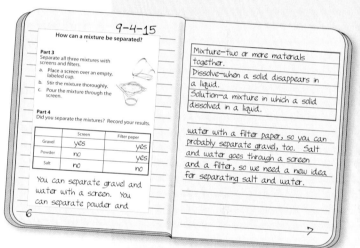

You will find the duplication masters for grades 1–6
presented in notebook format. They are reduced in
size (two copies to a standard sheet) for placement
(glue or tape) into a bound composition book. Full-
size duplication masters are also available on FOSSweb.
Student work is entered partly in spaces provided on
the notebook sheets and partly on adjacent blank sheets.

## Reading in *FOSS Science Resources*

*FOSS Science Resources* emphasizes expository articles and biographical
sketches. FOSS suggests that the reading be completed during
language-arts time. When language-arts skills and methods are
embedded in content material that relates to the authentic experience
students have had during the FOSS active-learning sessions, students are
interested, and they get more meaning from the text material.

## Assessing Progress

The FOSS assessment system includes both formative and summative assessments. Formative assessments monitor learning during the process of instruction. They measure progress, provide information about learning, and are generally diagnostic. Summative assessment looks at the learning after instruction is completed, and it measures achievement.

Formative assessment in FOSS, called **embedded assessment**, occurs on a daily basis. You observe action during class or review notebooks after class. Embedded assessment provides continuous monitoring of students' learning and helps you make decisions about whether to review, extend, or move on to the next idea to be covered. The embedded assessments are based on authentic work produced by students during the course of participating in the FOSS activities. Students do their science, and you look at their notebook entries. Embedded assessment is assessment *for* learning, not assessment *of* learning.

**Benchmark assessments** are short summative assessments given at the end of each investigation. These I–Checks are actually hybrid tools: they provide summative information about students' achievement, and because they occur soon after teaching each investigation, they can be used diagnostically as well. The assessment items do not simply identify whether a student knows a piece of science content. The items identify the depth to which students understand science concepts and principles and the extent to which students can apply that understanding. Since the output from the benchmark assessments is descriptive and complex, it can be used for formative as well as summative purposes.

## Taking FOSS Outdoors

FOSS throws open the classroom door and proclaims the entire school campus to be the science classroom. The true value of science knowledge is its usefulness in the real world and not just in the classroom. Taking regular excursions into the immediate outdoor environment has many benefits. First of all, it provides opportunities for students to apply things they learned in the classroom to novel situations. When students are able to transfer knowledge of scientific principles to natural systems, they experience a sense of accomplishment.

In addition to transfer and application, students can learn things outdoors that they are not able to learn indoors. The most important object of inquiry outdoors is the outdoors itself. To today's youth, the outdoors is something to pass through as quickly as possible to get to the next human-managed place. For many, engagement with the outdoors and natural systems must be intentional, at least at first. With repeated visits to familiar outdoor learning environments, students may first develop comfort in the outdoors, and then a desire to embrace and understand natural systems.

The last part of most investigations is an outdoor experience. Venturing out will require courage the first time or two you mount an outdoor expedition. It will confuse students as they struggle to find the right behavior that is a compromise between classroom rigor and diligence and the freedom of recreation. With persistence, you will reap rewards—you might be amazed by the transformation of students with behavior issues in the classroom who become your insightful observers and leaders in the schoolyard environment.

## Science-Centered Language Development

The FOSS active investigations, science notebooks, *FOSS Science Resources* articles, and formative assessments provide rich contexts in which students develop and exercise thinking and communication. These elements are essential for effective instruction in both science and language arts—students experience the natural world in real and authentic ways and use language to inquire, process information, and communicate their thinking about scientific phenomena. FOSS refers to this development of language process and skills within the context of science as science-centered language development.

There are many ways to integrate language into science investigations. The most effective integration depends on the type of investigation, the experience of students, the language skills and needs of students, and the language objectives that you deem important at the time. The Science-Centered Language Development chapter is a library of resources and strategies for you to use. The chapter describes how literacy strategies are integrated purposefully into the FOSS investigations, gives suggestions for additional literacy strategies that both enhance students' learning in science and develop or exercise English-language literacy skills, and develops science vocabulary with scaffolding strategies for supporting all learners.

# FOSSweb and Technology

FOSS is committed to providing a rich, accessible technology experience for all FOSS users. FOSSweb is the Internet access to FOSS digital resources. It provides enrichment for students and support for teachers, administrators, and families who are actively involved in implementing and enjoying FOSS materials.

## Technology to Engage Students at School and at Home

**Multimedia activities.** These include virtual investigations and student tutorials to support students who have difficulties or who have been absent.

**FOSS Science Resources.** The student reading book is available as an audio book on FOSSweb. In addition, as premium content, *FOSS Science Resources* is available as an eBook.

**Home/school connection.** Each module includes a letter to families that provides an overview of the goals and objectives of the module available in print on FOSSweb.

**Student media library.** A variety of media enhance students' learning, including photos, videos, audio versions of student books, and frequently asked science questions.

**Recommended books and websites.** FOSS has reviewed print books and digital resources that are appropriate for students and prepared a list of these media resources.

**Class pages.** Teachers with a FOSSweb account can set up class pages with notes and assignments for students and families to access online.

## Technology to Support Teachers

**Teacher-preparation video.** The video presents information to help you prepare for a module, including detailed investigation information and equipment setup and use.

**Science-notebook masters and teacher masters.** All notebook masters and teacher masters used in the modules are available digitally on FOSSweb for downloading and for projection during class. These sheets are available in English and Spanish.

**Assessment masters.** The benchmark assessment masters for grades 1–6 (I-Checks) are available in English and Spanish.

**Focus questions.** The focus questions for each investigation are formatted for classroom projection and for printing onto 1" × 2⅝" mailing labels that students can glue into their science notebooks.

**Equipment photo cards.** The cards provide labeled photos of equipment supplied in the FOSS kit.

**Materials Safety Data Sheets (MSDS).** These sheets have information from materials manufacturers on handling and disposal of materials.

**Module summary.** The summary describes each investigation in a module, including major concepts developed.

**Module updates.** These are important updates related to the teacher materials, student equipment, and safety guidelines.

**Module teaching notes.** These notes include teaching suggestions and enhancements to the module, sent in by experienced FOSS users.

**Streaming video.** Some video clips are part of the instruction in the investigation, and others extend concepts presented in a module.

**Resources by investigation.** This digital listing provides online links to notebook sheets, assessment and teacher masters, and multimedia for each investigation of a module, for projection in the classroom.

**Interactive whiteboard resources.** You can use these slide shows and other resources with an interactive whiteboard.

**Teacher Resources chapters.** FOSSweb provides PDF files of these chapters in *Teacher Resources*—Science Notebooks, Science-Centered Language Development, Taking FOSS Outdoors, and FOSSweb and Technology.

***Investigations eGuide.*** The eGuide is the complete *FOSS Investigations Guide* component of the *Teacher Toolkit* in an electronic web-based format, allowing access from any Internet-enabled computer.

***FOSSmap and online assessments.*** A computerized assessment program, called FOSSmap, provides a system for students to take assessments online, and for you to review those assessments online and to assign tutorial sessions for individual students based on assessment performance. After students have completed a benchmark assessment, FOSSmap automatically codes the multiple-choice, multiple-answer, and short-answer questions. Once the codes are in the FOSSmap program, you can generate and display several reports.

The *Code-Frequency Report* is a bar graph showing how many students received each code. This graph makes it easy to see which items might need further instruction.

In the *Class-by-Item Report*, information for each item is presented in a text format that indicates the names and percentages of students who selected each answer, what code (score) they received, and a description of what students know or need help with based on how they answered each item.

The *Class-by-Level Report* describes four levels of achievement. It lists class percentages and students who achieved each level.

The *Class-Frequency Report* has bar graphs indicating how many students achieved each level. The survey and posttest are shown on the same page for easy comparison.

The *Student-by-Item Report* is available for each student. It provides information about what the student knows or what he or she needs to work on.

The *Student Assessment Summary* bar graph indicates the level achieved by individual students on all the assessments taken up to any point in the module. This graph makes it easy to compare achievement on the survey and posttest as well as on each I-Check.

***Tutorials.*** You can assign online tutorials to individual students, based on how each student answers questions on the I-Checks and posttest. The *Student-by-Item Report*, generated by FOSSmap, indicates the tutorials specifically targeted to help individual students to refine their understandings. Tutorials are an excellent tool for differentiating instruction and are available to students at any time on FOSSweb.

# FOSS Introduction

## FOSS K–8 SCOPE AND SEQUENCE

| Grade | Physical Science | Earth Science | Life Science |
|---|---|---|---|
| 6–8 | Electronics<br>Chemical Interactions<br>Force and Motion | Planetary Science<br>Earth History<br>Weather and Water | Human Brain and Senses<br>Populations and Ecosystems<br>Diversity of Life |
| 4–6 | Mixtures and Solutions<br>Motion, Force, and Models<br>Energy and Electromagnetism | Weather on Earth<br>Sun, Moon, and Planets<br>Soils, Rocks, and Landforms | Living Systems<br>Environments |
| 3 | Measuring Matter | Water | Structures of Life |
| 1–2 | Balance and Motion<br>Solids and Liquids | Air and Weather<br>Pebbles, Sand, and Silt | Insects and Plants<br>Plants and Animals |
| K | Materials in Our World | Trees and Weather | Animals Two by Two |

FOSS is a research-based science curriculum for grades K–8 developed at the Lawrence Hall of Science, University of California, Berkeley. FOSS is also an ongoing research project dedicated to improving the learning and teaching of science. The FOSS project began over 25 years ago during a time of growing concern that our nation was not providing young students with an adequate science education. The FOSS Program materials are designed to meet the challenge of providing meaningful science education for all students in diverse American classrooms and to prepare them for life in the 21st century. Development of the FOSS Program was, and continues to be, guided by advances in the understanding of how people think and learn.

With the initial support of the National Science Foundation and continued support from the University of California, Berkeley, and School Specialty, Inc., the FOSS Program has evolved into a curriculum for all students and their teachers, grades K–8. The current editions of FOSS are the result of a rich collaboration between the FOSS/Lawrence Hall of Science development staff; the FOSS product development team at Delta Education; assessment specialists, educational researchers, and scientists; dedicated professionals in the classroom and their students, administrators, and families.

We acknowledge the thousands of FOSS educators who have embraced the notion that science is an active process, and we thank them for their significant contributions to the development and implementation of the FOSS Program.

# Science Notebooks
# in Grades K-2

Enrico Fermi's laboratory notebook, 1941

Source: Special Collections Research Center, University of Chicago Library

What are evergreen trees?
It is a tree.
does not lose
all its leaves.

Student notebook from the Trees and Weather Module

# INTRODUCTION

A scientist's notebook is a detailed record of his or her engagement with scientific phenomena. It is a personal representation of experiences, observations, and thinking—an integral part of the process of doing scientific work. A scientist's notebook is a continuously updated history of the development of scientific knowledge and reasoning. FOSS students are young scientists; they incorporate notebooks into their science learning.

This chapter is designed to be a resource for teachers who are incorporating notebooks into their classroom practice. For teachers just beginning to use notebooks, the Getting Started section in this chapter suggests how to set up the notebooks, and the *Investigations Guide* cues you when to engage students with the notebooks during the investigation. For more information on specific types of notebook entries, the subsections in the Notebook Components sections include strategies to differentiate instruction for various ability levels.

## Contents

# NOTEBOOK BENEFITS

Engaging in active science is one part experience and two parts making sense of the experience. Science notebooks help students with the sense-making part. Science notebooks assist with documentation and cognitive engagement. For teachers, notebooks are tools for gaining insight into students' thinking. Notebooks inform and refine instructional practice.

## Benefits to Students

**Benefits to Students**
- *Documentation*
- *Reference document*
- *Cognitive engagement*

***Documentation.*** Science provides an authentic experience for students to develop their documentation skills. In the primary classroom, getting students to use a notebook will introduce the powerful skills of information organization. Students document their experiences, data, and thinking during each investigation. They create simple tables, graphs, charts, drawings, and labeled illustrations as standard means for representing and displaying data. At first, students will look at their science notebooks as little more than a random collection of words and pictures. Each notebook page represents an isolated activity. As students become more accomplished at keeping notebooks, their documentation will become better organized and efficient. In time and with some guidance, students will adopt a deeper understanding of their collections as integrated records of their learning.

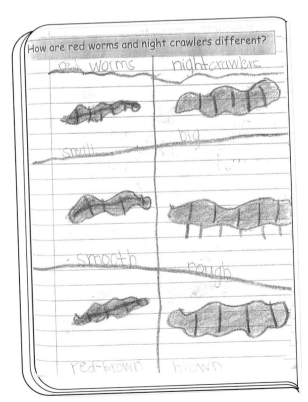

**Kindergarten entry from the Animals Two by Two Module**

*Reference document.* When data are displayed in functional ways, students can think about the data more effectively. Even with young students, a well-kept notebook is a useful reference document. When students have forgotten a fact about an insect or a plant that they learned earlier in their studies, they can look it up. Learning to trust a personal record of previous discoveries and knowledge structures is important.

A complete and accurate record allows students to reconstruct the sequence of learning events to "relive" the experience. Discussions about science among students; students and teachers; or students, teachers, and families have more meaning when they are supported by authentic documentation in students' notebooks.

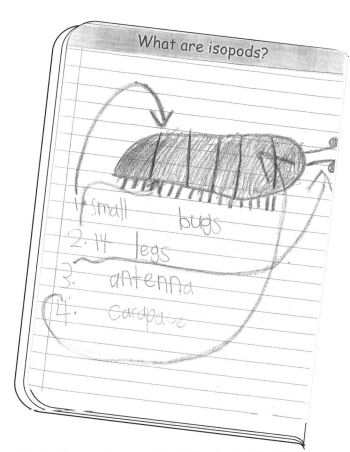

**Labeled drawing from the Animals Two by Two Module**

**Cognitive engagement.** Once data are recorded and organized in an efficient manner in science notebooks, students can think about the data to draw conclusions about the way the world works. Their data, based on their experiences and observations, are the raw materials that students use to forge concepts and relationships.

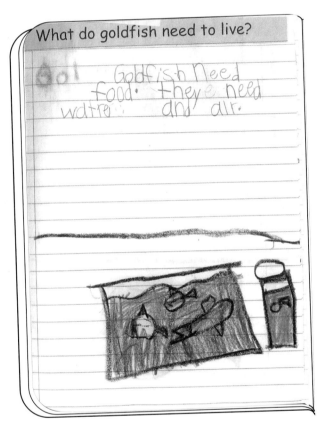

Responding to a focus question from the Animals Two by Two Module with a drawing and words

# Benefits to Teachers

In FOSS, the unit of instruction is the module—a sequence of conceptually related learning experiences that leads to a set of learning outcomes. A science notebook helps you think about and communicate the conceptual structure of the module you are teaching.

**Assessment.** From the assessment point of view, a science notebook is a collection of student-generated artifacts that exhibit learning. You can assess student skills, such as using drawings to record data, while students are working with materials. At other times, you collect the notebooks and review them in greater detail. The displays of data and analytical work, such as responses to focus questions, provide a measure of the quality and quantity of student learning. The notebook itself should not be graded. However, the notebook can be considered as one component of a student's overall performance in science.

**Medium for feedback.** The science notebook is an excellent medium for providing feedback to individual students regarding their work. Some students may be able to read a teacher comment written on a self-stick note, think about the issue, and respond. Other students may need oral feedback individually or in a small-group situation. This feedback might include additional modeling to help students make more accurate drawings, revisiting some important vocabulary, or introducing strategies to help students better communicate their thinking.

**Focus for professional discussions.** The science notebook acts as a focal point for discussion about students' learning at several levels. It can be reviewed and discussed during parent conferences. Science notebooks can be the focus of three-way discussions among students, teachers, and principals to ensure that all members of the school science community agree about what kinds of student work are valued and what level of performance to expect. Science notebooks shared among teachers in a study group or other professional-development environment can serve as a reflective tool that informs teachers of students' ability to demonstrate recording techniques, individual styles, various levels of good-quality work, and so on. Just as students can learn notebook strategies from one another, teachers can learn notebook skills from one another.

**Benefits to Teachers**
- *Assessment*
- *Medium for feedback*
- *Focus for professional discussions*
- *Refinement of practice*

A teacher provides feedback to a student.

**Refinement of practice.** As teachers, we are constantly looking for ways to improve instructional practices to increase students' understanding. Your use of the notebook should change over time. In the beginning, the focus will be on the notebook itself—what it looks like, what goes in it. As you become more comfortable with the notebook, the attention shifts to what students are learning. When this happens, you begin to consider how much scaffolding to provide to different students, how to use evidence of learning to differentiate instruction, and how to modify instruction to refine students' understanding.

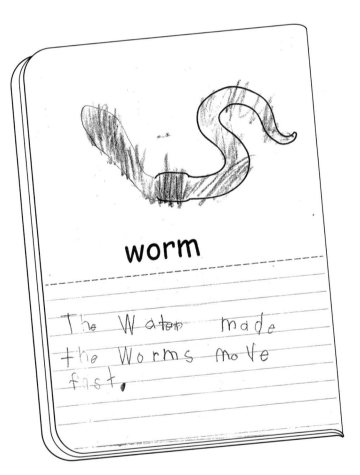

Kindergarten entry from the Animals Two by Two Module

# GETTING STARTED

Starting in kindergarten, students are expected to make detailed, thoughtful records of their science inquiries. While this may seem like a lofty goal, with some patience and thoughtful support, both teachers and students can learn how to use science notebooks effectively.

A major goal for using notebooks is to establish habits that will enable students to collect data and make sense of them. Use of the notebook must be flexible enough to allow students room to grow and supportive enough for students to be successful from the start. The format should be simple and the information meaningful to students. The notebook includes student drawings, simple writing in the form of individual words and short phrases, and a variety of visual and tactile artifacts. When students thumb through their notebooks, they are reminded of the objects and organisms they observed and their interactions with them.

## Notebook Format

Delta Education sells bound science notebooks that include printed notebook sheets specific for each module. These consumable, preprinted notebooks provide an efficient, supportive approach to early-childhood notebook keeping.

The *Teacher Resources* component of the FOSS *Teacher Toolkit* includes duplication masters for the same notebook sheets that are bound into the consumable notebooks. You can use these sheets to prepare an analogous notebook or to design a customized version.

In an autonomous approach, students create their entire science notebooks from blank pages in bound composition books. Students can glue or tape the provided notebook sheets into their notebooks, as well as create their own notebook entries. This level of notebook use will not be realized quickly and will require modeling by the teacher to provide enough structure to make the notebook useful. It will likely require systematic development by an entire teaching staff over several years.

You might choose to have a separate notebook for each module or one notebook for the entire year. (See the sidebar for the advantages of each.) Students will need about 30 pages (60 sides) for a typical module.

**Advantages of One Notebook per Module:**
- *Easy to replace if lost*
- *Lower cost*
- *Fewer pages*

**Advantages of One Notebook per Year:**
- *Easy to refer to prior activities*
- *Easy to see growth over time*

## Organization of Notebooks

Two organizational components of the notebook should be planned right from the outset for primary students—page numbering and documentation. Two additional organizational components—a table of contents and an index—might be included only in the class notebook (detailed in the Supporting Students section) or in student notebooks toward the end of second grade. Not all organizational structures need to be present in individual student notebooks in the primary grades.

***Page numbering.*** Each page should have a number. These can be applied to the pages, front to back, and referenced in the table of contents as the notebook progresses, or small blocks of pages can be prenumbered (pages 1–5 initially, pages 6–10 later, and so on) at appropriate times in the module.

A parent volunteer could number the pages. If students number them, monitor their work to make sure they don't skip pages or misnumber them.

***Date, title, and other conditions.*** Each time students make a new entry, they should record certain information. At the very minimum, they should record the date and a title. More complete documentation might include the time; day of the week; team members; and if appropriate, weather conditions. When introducing a new condition to students, such as recording the names of team members, it is important to discuss why students are recording the information so that they understand the relevancy.

Some classes start each new entry at the top of the next available page. Others simply leave a modest space and enter the information right before the new entry.

**Table of contents.** If students keep a table of contents in their own notebooks, they should reserve the first two pages of the notebook for it. You will need to remind students to add to it systematically as you proceed through the module. The table of contents can be based on the names of the investigations in the module, the specific activities undertaken, the concepts learned, or some other schema that makes sense to everyone.

You might provide students with a preprinted table of contents without page numbers. As students work through each investigation, they record the relevant page numbers in their table of contents. If students are making their own table of contents, they should keep it fairly simple.

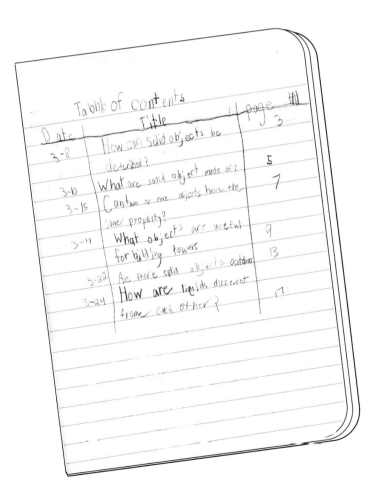

A table of contents for the Solids and Liquids Module

**Index.** Scientific academic language is important. FOSS strives to have students use precise, accurate vocabulary at all times in their writing and conversations. Key words can be displayed using a pocket chart, word wall, or written on index cards kept in boxes at each table. Another support to assist with acquisition of the scientific vocabulary is to introduce an index in the class notebook. It is not usually possible to enter the words in alphabetical order, since they will be acquired as the module advances. Instead, assign a block of letters to each of several index pages at the back of the class notebook (A–E, F–K, etc.); you or students can enter keys words. Students write the new vocabulary word or phrase in the appropriate square and tag it with the number of the page on which the word is defined in the notebook.

Including an index in the class notebook is a long-term time investment and can be overwhelming for the beginning notebook user. It may be better to forgo the index and use just a word wall to work with vocabulary initially.

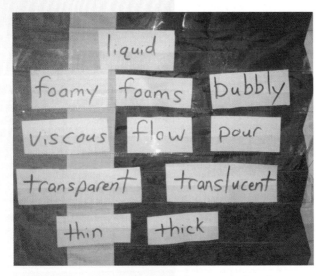

Pocket charts can be used to introduce vocabulary for students to include in their notebooks.

## Notebook Entries

As students engage in scientific exploration, they will make entries in their notebooks. They might use a prepared notebook sheet or a more free-form entry. Students frequently respond to a focus question with a drawing or a simple written entry. Kindergartners may write single words; first and second graders will write simple observations and summary ideas, using the new vocabulary in their entries. These notebook entries allow early-childhood students to relive and describe their science experiences as they turn the pages in their notebooks.

Typically, the rules of grammar and spelling are relaxed when making notebook entries so as not to inhibit the flow of creative expression. Encourage students to use many means of recording and communicating besides writing, including charts, graphs, drawings, color codes, numbers, and images attached to the notebook pages. By exploring many options for making notebook entries, each student will find his or her most efficient, expressive way to capture and organize information for later retrieval.

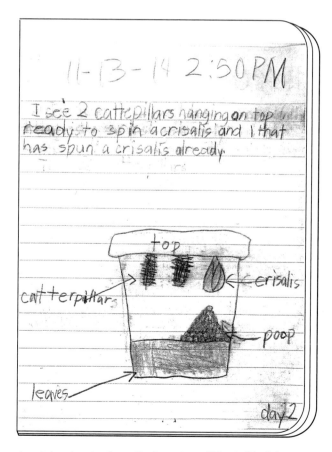

**A notebook entry from the Insects and Plants Module**

## Supporting Students

Elementary classrooms contain students with a range of abilities, which is important to take into account when thinking about strategies for implementing science notebooks. Students need to have successful early experiences with notebooks. This requires planning. For younger students, a blank notebook may be intimidating, and they will look to you for guidance. FOSS teachers have had success using different supports and scaffolds to help transform the blank notebook into a valuable reference tool.

***Class notebook.*** You can create a class notebook to document scientific explorations as a way to model the various notebook components. Use a chart-paper tablet so that the pages can be flipped back and forth, and make it accessible at all times as a student reference. Students can emulate the class notebook in their own personal notebooks. Initially, individual notebooks will look quite similar to the class notebook. It is not the intent that students' notebooks be identical to the class notebook.

***Scaffolds.*** Supports and scaffolds differ in one way. Supports are always available for students to access, such as allowing students access to a class notebook. Scaffolds are available just when the student needs them and will vary from student to student and from investigation to investigation. Scaffolds are meant to provide structure to a notebook entry and allow students to insert their observations into that structure. As the year progresses, the scaffolds change to allow for more student initiative. Scaffolds include

- **Sentence starters** or **drawing starters** provide a beginning point for a notebook entry.

- **Frames** provide more support but leave specific gaps for students to complete. Here's an example: "We planted _____ seeds and used _____ to water them."

- The suggested **notebook sheets** can guide students to record observations and data. The notebook sheets also guide thinking.

---

**TEACHING NOTE**

*Use of the class notebook should be thoughtfully timed. Doing a class-notebook entry at the end of an activity is helpful to teach the components of a notebook, yet allows you to see what students do on their own. If you want to model a specific notebook strategy, use the class notebook during the activity.*

---

**Think-alouds.** Think-alouds help explain the decision-making process practiced by a savvy notebook user. They verbalize the thoughts used to create a particular notebook entry. For example, if students have recorded observations about one type of rock and are going to observe a second type, you might say,

*I am going to observe another kind of rock. I'm going to look back to see how I recorded rock information before. I see that I made a large, detailed drawing. I described the texture, size, and color of the rock, too. So now I think I will make a drawing of the new rock. I'm going to record the texture, size, and color, too.*

*Now I know that one way I can get ideas for what to write in my notebook is to look back at observations I wrote before.*

**Providing time to record.** When young students are engaged in active science, their efforts are focused on the materials, not the notebook. Students need this time to explore, and many will not open their notebooks and record observations, even with prompting. Students need separate time to record observations that fully document their discoveries. Some teachers have found it easier to leave the materials on the table and have students bring their notebooks to a common writing area. Then the teacher revisits the focus question or task and provides a few minutes for students to record in their notebooks.

**Dictation.** Students could dictate specific information to an adult. The adult writes the information in the notebook for the student. Or the adult could write the sentence, using a highlighter, and students could trace the words, using a pencil.

## Ownership

A student's science notebook can be personal or public. If the notebook is personal, the student decides how accessible his or her work is to other students. If ownership falls at the opposite extreme, everything is public, and anyone can look at the contents of anyone else's notebook at any time. In practice, most classroom cultures establish a middle ground in which a student's notebook is substantially personal, but the teacher claims free access to the student's work and can request that students share notebooks with one another and with the whole class from time to time.

**Notebook Components**

- *Planning the investigation*
- *Data acquisition and organization*
- *Making sense of data*
- *Next-step strategies*

# NOTEBOOK COMPONENTS

A few components give the science notebook conceptual shape and direction. These components don't prescribe a step-by-step procedure for how to prepare the notebook, but they do provide some overall guidance.

The general arc of an investigation starts with a question or challenge, and then proceeds with an activity, data acquisition, sense making, and next steps. The science notebook should record important observations and thoughts along the way. It may be useful to keep these four components in mind as you systematically guide students through their notebook entries.

## Planning the Investigation

Typically at the start of a new activity, the first notebook entry is a focus question, which students glue or transcribe into their notebooks. The focus question determines the kinds of data to be collected and the procedures that will yield those data. Depending on the timing and their previous experiences, students may be asked to record a prediction related to the focus question.

Notebook entry with focus question from the Materials in Our World Module

***Focus question.*** Each part of each investigation starts with a focus question or challenge. The focus question establishes the direction and conceptual challenge for the activity. Write or project it on the board or on the chart for students to transcribe into their notebooks, or give them photocopied strips of the focus question to tape or glue into their notebooks. The focus-question strips are distributed as needed. Some teachers give students adhesive-backed labels with the focus questions printed on them.

> 3. **How can you sink wood?**
> Write the focus question on the chart, and have students read it together.
>
> ➤ *How can you sink wood?*

**TEACHING NOTE**

*Student-developed plans appear infrequently in grades K–2. Asking students to record plans for every investigation is not recommended.*

***Plans and procedures.*** Students may plan their investigation. The planning may be detailed or informal, depending on the requirement of the investigation. These plans take time to develop and additional time to document in the notebook. A brief class discussion of the procedure may lead to a sentence or two recorded in the class notebook. This will be sufficient for many of the investigations.

***Predictions.*** Depending on the content and the focus question, students may be able to make a prediction. When they make predictions, they are attempting to relate prior experiences to the question posed. Providing students with a frame can help them explain the rationale behind their predictions. A frame to help with stating a prediction is "I think that _____ because _____."

## Data Acquisition and Organization

Data are the bits of information (observations) from which scientists construct ideas about the structure and behaviors of the natural world. Because observation is the starting point for answering the focus question, data records should be

- clearly related to the focus question;

- accurate and precise;

- organized for efficient reference.

Data handling can have two phases: data acquisition and data display. Data acquisition is making observations and recording data. The data record can be composed of words, phrases, numbers, and/or drawings. Data display is reorganizing the data in a logical way to facilitate thinking. The display can take the form of narratives, drawings, artifacts, tables, graphs, images, or other graphic organizers. Early in a student's experience with notebooks, the record may be disorganized and incomplete, and the display will need guidance. Students will need support to determine what form of recording to use in various situations and how best to display the data for analysis.

***Narratives.*** The most intuitive approach to recording data for most students is narrative—using words, sentence fragments, and numbers in a more or less sequential manner. As students make a new observation, they record it right after the previous entry, followed by the next observation, and so on. Some observations, such as the changes observed in a mealworm, are appropriately recorded in narrative form.

Sentence frames provide a way for students to record their data. If students are nonwriters, they can dictate their observations, and you can write their observations in their notebooks, using a highlighter. Students can then trace the highlighted words.

**A narrative observation from the Solids and Liquids Module**

***Drawings.*** When students observe organisms or systems, a labeled illustration is a very efficient way to record data. A picture is worth a thousand words, and a labeled picture is even more useful.

Some young students may initially prefer drawing their observations, while others may struggle to do so. When students make drawings, it can be helpful to suggest an acronym for making useful drawings. Accurate, big, colorful, and detailed (ABCD) drawings can capture structures of an organism, a balanced object, or an observation of a liquid. Think-alouds can also help students gain insight about not only what to draw but also when a drawing is useful.

It is not unusual for students to embellish their drawings by adding features such as smiles to flowers and living organisms. While this may be appropriate for creative expression, scientific illustrations should not be anthropomorphized. Give students feedback about making authentic observations.

***Artifacts.*** Occasionally, the results of an investigation produce three-dimensional products that students can tape or glue directly into their science notebooks. Rubbings, disassembled fabrics, sand, minerals, seeds, and so on can become a permanent part of the record of learning.

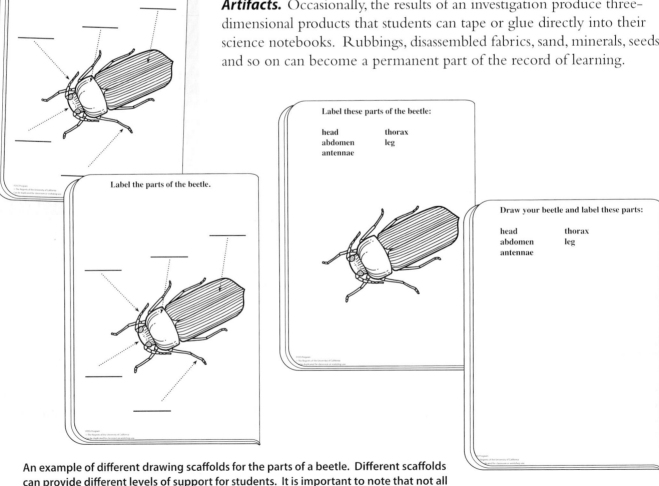

An example of different drawing scaffolds for the parts of a beetle. Different scaffolds can provide different levels of support for students. It is important to note that not all students need the same level of support.

**Tables.** When students make similar observations about a series of objects, such as properties of solid objects, a table with columns is an efficient recording method. The two-dimensional table makes it easy to compare the properties of all the objects under investigation.

Often, the preprinted notebook sheet provides a blank table. Students can quickly enter information on the notebook sheet. As students take on more independence in their notebooks, discussions about the column headings or the purpose of the tables shift the focus from filling in the table to the purpose the table serves.

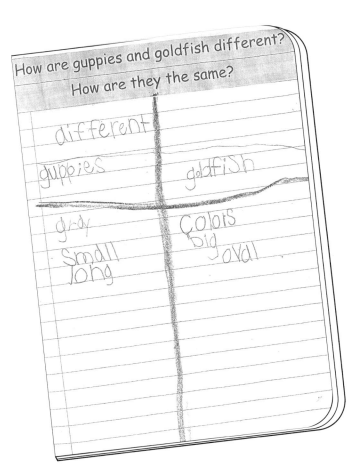

A simple table from the Animals Two by Two Module

**Graphs and graphics.** Reorganizing data into a logical, easy-to-use graphic is an important phase of data analysis. Bar graphs allow easy comparison. Additional graphic tools, such as concept maps and life cycles, help students make connections between data accrued during investigations.

For kindergarten students, you will need to model and scaffold graphs and graphics when students are ready. Visuals displayed in students' notebooks should also appear in a larger format on a whiteboard, projected display, or in the class notebook. You can use this larger display to connect organized data to the content students are learning.

**Images.** Digital photos of plants, rocks, and the results of investigations can be great additions to the science notebook.

# Making Sense of Data

The third component of an investigation involves analyzing the data to learn something about the natural world. Establishing the habit of thinking about the data collected and using them to help us answer a question is important.

Most of the sense making in the primary classroom takes place during whole-group discussions when students share and discuss the observations they made while investigating. Questions are asked to help students interpret and analyze data in order to build conceptual understanding. Encourage students to use new vocabulary when they are sharing and making sense of their data. These words should be accessible to all students in the class notebook and displayed in the room. When students have limited written language skills, this oral discussion is important. This sharing is essential and is described in detail in the *Investigations Guide*. After sharing observations, the class revisits the focus question. Students flip back in their notebooks and use their data to discuss their answers to the question. You scaffold the discussion, and use appropriate language-development strategies.

---

8. **Ask questions to guide discussion**
   Ask questions to guide students' observations and discussion.

   ➤ *Were you able to sink the wood by attaching paper clips?*

   ➤ *How many paper clips did you use to sink the wood?*

   ➤ *Let's compare the two samples. Does it take the same number of paper clips to sink both kinds of wood?*

   ➤ *Does it make a difference where you put the paper clips on the wood? All on one side? Evenly distributed around all sides?*

---

After the sense-making discussion, students might review relevant vocabulary. Then they answer the focus question in their notebooks. In the beginning, you might model this writing in a class notebook, or students might work in small groups to write a collaborative response. Students could also make a drawing as a response to a focus question. As students become more proficient writers, they will begin to record their own written responses to the focus question.

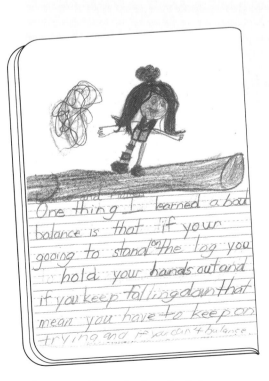

**A sense-making entry from the Balance and Motion Module**

Making sense of data is an opportunity for students to grapple with scientific concepts. The expectation is that all students will engage in this component. In many instances, using assistive structures, such as frames and prompts to guide the development of a coherent and complete response to the focus question, will help establish this expectation.

**Thinking with evidence.** In the primary classroom, students are expected to explain their thinking and provide some supporting evidence. While their explanations and evidence may be relatively simple, they will provide you with evidence of student understanding. A student might conclude that objects that have a round surface will roll because a ball and a can both rolled and they have round surfaces. The evidence should refer to specific observations, measurements, and so on.

For example, an investigation in the **Animals Two by Two Module** poses the focus question

➤ *What is the difference between red worms and night crawlers?*

Students observe and record, using the class notebook as a model. You create a Venn diagram, with input from students during discussion that compares the two types of worms. Students hear the focus question again, and they discuss their thinking in their groups. You write this frame in the class notebook

*One difference between a red worm and a night crawler is _____ . I know this because _____ .*

All students get a preprinted frame to glue into their notebooks and answer independently. Be careful not to display conclusions or other sense-making entries in a class notebook before students make their own entries. Otherwise, assessment of student thinking becomes difficult, as a student may copy the class-notebook response with little understanding of the meaning.

### TEACHING NOTE

*If students respond verbally, it is important to record those responses in the science notebook to establish that notebooks are a place to document understandings.*

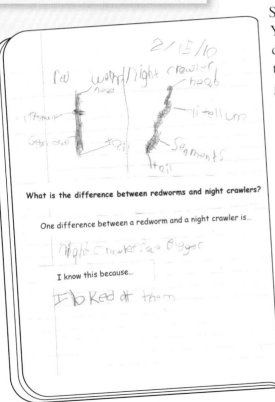

An answer to a focus question from the Animals Two by Two Module

**Frames and prompts.** Providing frames helps students organize their thinking. The frame provides a communication structure that allows students to focus on thinking about the science involved. This could be identifying the difference between two worms, students' thoughts about which types of objects roll, or how people can change the shape of wood. The frame does not do the thinking for students, but allows them to respond to the focus question in a clear, coherent manner.

- *One difference between the red worm and the night crawler is _____ .*

- *I noticed that all the things that rolled _____ .*

- *I know this because _____ .*

**I wonder.** Does the investigation connect to a student's personal interests? Or does the outcome suggest a question or pique a student's curiosity? Providing time for students to write "I wonder" statements or questions supports the idea that the pursuit of scientific knowledge does not end with the day's investigation. The notebook is an excellent place to capture students' musings and for students to record thoughts that might otherwise be lost.

**Wrap-up/warm-up.** At the end of each investigation part or at the beginning of the next part, students will engage in a wrap-up or warm-up. This is another opportunity for students to revisit the content of the investigation. As they discuss their responses to the focus question with a partner, students may choose to edit their responses or add fresh information. This should be encouraged.

---

**13. Share notebook entries**

Conclude Part 4 or start Part 5 by having students share notebook entries. Ask students to open their science notebooks to the most recent entry. Read the focus question together as a class.

➤ *How can you sink wood?*

Ask students to pair up with a partner to

- share their answers to the focus question;
- explain their drawings.

---

**TEACHING NOTE**

*Students' learning can be assessed only at the level in which it was done. If students worked in groups to answer the focus question, it is difficult to assess individual understanding. Similarly, providing a frame to guide a student response provides evidence on what students can do at a supported level, not at an independent level.*

**TEACHING NOTE**

*These next-step strategies should be kept simple for primary students. The key idea is that students can revise their responses after gaining more information.*

## Next-Step Strategies

In each investigation, the *Investigations Guide* indicates an assessment opportunity and what to look for when examining students' work. The purpose of looking at students' work at this juncture is for formative, or embedded, assessment, *not* for grading. Look for patterns in students' understanding by collecting and sorting the notebooks. If the patterns indicate that students need additional help with communication or with content, you might want to select a next-step strategy before going on to the next part. This process of looking at students' work is described in more detail in the Assessment chapter.

A next-step strategy is an instructional tool designed to help students clarify their thinking and usually takes place before the start of the next investigation part. A strategy is selected based on students' needs. It may be that a student needs to communicate his or her thinking more efficiently or accurately or to use scientific vocabulary. A student may need to think about the concept in a different way. Because many young students are not able to articulate their thinking well in writing, it can be difficult to discern the area of need.

What follows is a collection of next-step strategies that teachers have used successfully with groups of students to address areas of need. These strategies are flexible enough to use in different groupings and can be modified to meet your students' needs.

**Teacher feedback.** Students' writing often exposes weaknesses in students' understanding—or so it appears. It is important to check whether the flaw results from poor understanding of the science or from imprecise communication. When students are able to read your comments, you can use self-stick notes to provide constructive feedback or dig deeper into students' thinking. The note might pose a question designed to move a student's thinking forward or to clarify an explanation. The student acts independently on the question.

When students have not developed the reading skills necessary to act independently on written feedback, read the question or prompt to the student. Language skills are supported when students have the opportunity to connect the written feedback to what you read to them.

The most effective forms of feedback relate to the content of the work. Here are a couple of examples.

- *Label your drawing to show the parts of the plant.*

- *Tell me why you think you were able to balance the triangle and the arch.*

Nonspecific feedback (such as stars, smiley faces, and "good job!") and ambiguous critiques, (such as "try again," "put more thought into this," and "not enough,") are less effective. Feedback that guides students to think about the content of their work and gives suggestions for how to improve are productive instructional strategies. Here are some examples of useful generic feedback.

- *Use the science words in your answer.*

- *Can you tell me why you think that?*

- *Why do you think that happened?*

Students return to their notebooks and read or listen to the feedback at the start of the next investigation. They can discuss this feedback with a partner during the warm-up time and refine their responses. You could model this refinement as a think-aloud or by using the class notebook. Monitor students to ensure that they are acting on the feedback provided.

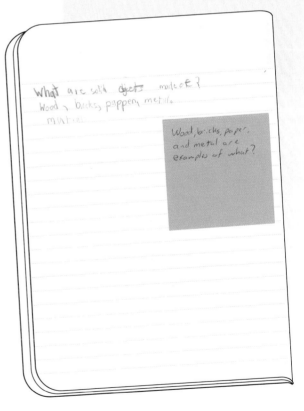

Students can respond to feedback by using a different color to show their new understanding.

**Review and critique anonymous student work.** Presenting work from other students can be a valuable learning tool for refining and improving the content and literacy of responses. Depending upon the culture of the class, you might present actual or simulated student work from a focus question or responses that reflect a common misconception, error, or exemplary work. Present it to the class in a common gathering area, such as on a rug, or display it electronically while students are at their seats. Present one simple response, such as a labeled drawing. Students then work in a group to discuss the merits and recommend improvements to the student response. In this process, students discuss what information is needed for a quality response. After critiquing other students' responses, students look at their own responses and refine their thinking. Students could also use a different-color crayon or pencil to make changes to their own responses.

**Key points.** Pose the focus question to the class, and, through discussion, elicit the key ideas or points that would completely answer the question. List only key words or brief phrases on the board. If you have already recorded the key points in the class notebook, revisit that

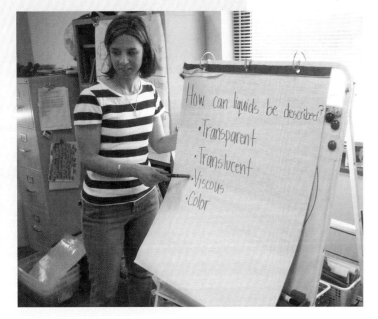

list as well. Once the class has agreed on the key points, students review their own responses, looking for the key points. You can guide this by calling out each key point on the list, and asking students to put a finger on it in their notebooks. If students need to add the key point, they can add it in another color.

**Mini-lessons.** Sometimes the data from sorting notebook entries reveal that students need some information repeated or specific guidance on a skill. A mini-lesson is a brief interaction with a group of students that addresses a specific area of need. You might have a group of students observe a mealworm more closely in order to count the number of segments, or give students a writing prompt and work with them to explain their thinking more clearly.

# WRITING OUTDOORS

Every time you go outdoors with students, you will have a slightly different experience. Naturally, the activity or task will be different, but other variables may change as well. The temperature, cloud cover, precipitation, moisture on the ground; other activities unexpectedly happening outside; students' comfort levels related to learning outdoors; and time of the school year are all aspects that could affect the activity and will certainly determine how you incorporate the use of notebooks. The following techniques are tried-and-true ways to help students learn how to write outdoors and to give them all the supplies they need to support their writing.

## Create "Desks"

Students need a firm writing surface. Students who write in composition notebooks with firm covers can simply fold them open to the pages they are writing on, rest them in the crook of their nonwriting arms, and hold them steady with their nonwriting hands—they can stand, sit, kneel, or lean against a wall to write. At the beginning of the school year, take a minute to model how to do this.

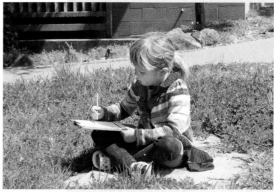

Many students feel most comfortable sitting down to write. Curbs, steps, wooden stumps or logs, rocks, and grass are places to sit while writing. Select a writing location that suits your students' comfort levels. Some students will not be comfortable sitting on the grass or ground at first. They will need to sit on something such as a curb, boulder, or wooden stump at the start of the year, but will eventually feel more comfortable with all aspects of the outdoor setting as the year moves along.

If students are using individual notebook sheets or notebooks with flimsy covers, you will likely want to buy or make clipboards. If you do not have clipboards, use a box cutter to cut cardboard to the proper size. Clamp a binder clip at the top to make a lightweight yet sturdy clipboard. If it gets ruined, no tears will be shed. If you're in the market for new clipboards, get the kind that are stackable and do not have a bulky clip. Ideally, all the clipboards will fit in one bag for portability and easy distribution.

If using a notebook sheet, simply put the sheet on the clipboard before going outdoors, and have students glue the sheet into their notebooks when you are back in the classroom. An elastic band around the bottom of the clipboard, or around a stiffer composition notebook, will help keep the paper from flapping around and becoming too weathered.

## Bring Writing Tools Outdoors

Almost always, students will set up their notebooks indoors so that they know what is expected of them outdoors. If students will be recording data, they will carry their pencils and notebooks or clipboards outdoors and hold on to them the entire time. Make sure students understand how and what to record.

You can bring chart paper outdoors. Roll up a blank piece of chart paper, grab some blue painter's tape, and stick the piece of paper to the school wall. You'll need to tape all four corners. Or set up a chart inside and clip it to a chain-link fence with binder clips or clothespins when you go outdoors.

Take along extra pencils, as many pencil points will break. Some teachers find it helpful to tie pencils onto clipboards. Pencils should be tucked between the clip and the notebook sheet so that students don't poke themselves or, more likely, accidentally break the pencil points.

Another option is to prepare a cloth bag containing small pencil sharpeners, extra pencils, and other science tools, such as vials, hand lenses, and rulers.

## Decide When to Write Outdoors

In general, notebook entries will be more detailed and more insightful if students can stay outdoors where the scientific exploration occurred. Sometimes, you will want to complete notebook entries indoors. If you are teaching the module early in the year when students are building up the routines for using the schoolyard, or if the weather is not ideal (a little chilly, raining, too hot, too windy), then you may want students to make notebook entries after returning to the classroom. If students are totally focused and in the moment, they can stay outdoors while they answer the focus question. If other students are outdoors playing, you may need to bring the class indoors to complete the written work. Only you will be able to determine what is best at the time.

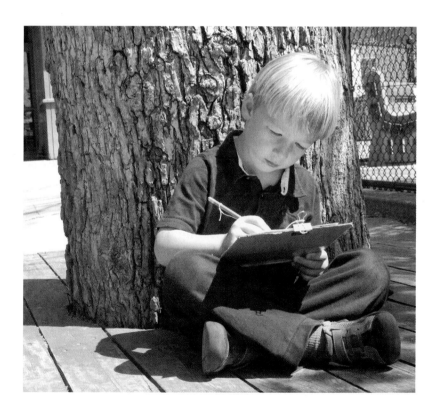

## CLOSING THOUGHTS

Engaging primary students in active science with notebooks provides a rich experience. Doing this successfully requires thoughtful interactions among students, materials, and natural phenomena. Initially, adding notebooks to your science teaching will require you to focus students' attention on how to set up the notebook, what types of entries students should make, and when students should be using their notebooks. You will establish conventions about where to record the date and title, where to keep notebooks, how to glue notebook sheets into notebooks, and when to record observations and thinking.

Once you are past these perfunctory issues, you can shift your focus to the amount of scaffolding to provide to students or to encouraging students to create their own notebook entries. During this time, you and your students are developing skills to improve the quality of notebook entries. These skills may include asking better questions to focus students' attention on a specific part of an organism or using color to enhance a drawing. Students begin to make entries with less prompting. They give more thought to supporting their responses to the focus question. When asked to make a derivative product, students thumb through their notebooks to find the needed information. The notebook becomes a tool for students to help recall their learning.

As students begin to document their thinking about focus questions and other queries, you may begin to wonder, "Should I be doing something with their notebooks?" This is when your focus shifts from the notebook as just something students use during science learning to the notebook as an assessment tool. Once everyone is comfortable recording the focus question and collecting data, you can take the next step of collecting notebooks and reading students' responses as a measure of not just how individual students are learning, but what the pervasive needs of students are. You choose next-step strategies that address students' needs before proceeding to the next investigation. The notebooks act as an assessment tool that lets you modify your science instruction.

This process will take time, discussions with colleagues, revisiting different sections of this chapter, and critical scrutiny of students' work before both you and your students are using notebooks to their full potential.

> **NOTE**
> For more on derivative products, see the Science-Centered Language Development chapter.

# Science-Centered Language Development

*Teams of science inquirers talk about and write about their questions, their tentative explanations, their relationships between evidence and explanations, and their reasons and judgments about public presentations and scientific arguments in behalf of their work. It is in the context of this kind of scientific activity that students' literacy of the spoken and written word develops along with the literacy of the phenomenon.*

**Hubert M. Dyasi, "Visions of Inquiry: Science"**

## Contents

# INTRODUCTION

In this chapter, we explore the intersection of science and language and the implications for effective science teaching and language development. We identify best practices in language arts instruction that support science learning and examine how learning science content and practices supports language development. The active investigations, science notebooks, *FOSS Science Resources* readings, and formative assessment activities in FOSS provide rich contexts in which students develop and exercise thinking processes and communication skills. Together, these elements comprise effective instruction in both science and language arts—students experience the natural world around them in real and authentic ways and use language to inquire, process information, and communicate their thinking about scientific phenomena. We refer to the development of language within the context of science as science-centered language development.

# Science-Centered Language Development

Language plays two crucial roles in science learning: (1) it facilitates the communication of conceptual and procedural knowledge, questions, and propositions (external, public), and (2) it mediates thinking, a process necessary for understanding (internal, private). These are also the ways scientists use language: to communicate with one another about their inquiries, procedures, and understandings; to transform their observations into ideas; and to create meaning and new ideas from their work and the work of others. For students, language development is intimately involved in their learning about the natural world. Science provides a real and engaging context for developing literacy, and language arts skills and strategies support conceptual development and scientific practices. For example, the skills and strategies used for reading comprehension, writing expository text, and oral discourse are applied when students are recording their observations, making sense of science content, and communicating their ideas. Students' use of language improves when they discuss, write, and read about the concepts explored in each investigation.

We begin our exploration of science and language by focusing on language functions and how specific language functions are used in science to facilitate information acquisition and processing (thinking). Then we address issues related to the specific language domains—speaking and listening, writing, and reading. Each section addresses

- how skills in that domain are developed and exercised in FOSS science investigations;

- literacy strategies that are integrated purposefully into the FOSS investigations;

- suggestions for additional literacy strategies that both enhance student learning in science and develop or exercise English-language literacy skills.

Following the domain discussions is a section on science-vocabulary development, with scaffolding strategies for supporting all learners. The last section covers language-development strategies specifically for English learners.

▶ **NOTE**
The term *English learners* refers to students who are learning to understand English. This includes students who speak English as a second language and native English speakers who need additional support to use language effectively.

# THE ROLE OF LANGUAGE IN SCIENTIFIC AND ENGINEERING PRACTICES

Language functions are the purpose for which speech or writing is used and involve both vocabulary and grammatical structure. Understanding and using language functions appropriately is important in effective communication. Students use numerous language functions in all disciplines to mediate communication and facilitate thinking (e.g., they plan, compare, discuss, apply, design, draw, and provide evidence).

In science, language functions facilitate the enactment of scientific and engineering practices. For example, when students are *collecting data*, they are using language functions to identify, label, enumerate, compare, estimate, and measure. When students are *constructing explanations*, they are using language functions to analyze, communicate, discuss, evaluate, and justify.

*A Framework for K–12 Science Education: Practices, Crosscutting Concepts, and Core Ideas* (National Research Council 2012) provides a "set of essential practices as essential for any education in the sciences and engineering." Each of these scientific and engineering practices requires the use of multiple language functions. Often, these language functions are part of an internal dialogue weighing the merits of various explanations—what we call thinking. The more language functions with which we are facile, the more effective and creative our thinking can be.

The scientific and engineering practices are listed below, along with a sample of the language functions that are exercised when effectively engaged in that practice. (Practices are bold; language functions are italic.)

## Asking questions and defining problems

- *Ask* questions about objects, organisms, systems, and events in the natural world (science) or define a problem (engineering).

## Planning and carrying out investigations; analyzing, and interpreting data

- *Plan* and conduct investigations.
- *Observe* and *record* data.
- *Measure* to extend the senses to acquire data.
- *Organize* observations (data), using numbers, words, images, and graphics.

**Examples of Language Functions**

*Analyze*
*Apply*
*Ask questions*
*Clarify*
*Classify*
*Communicate*
*Compare*
*Conclude*
*Construct*
*Critique*
*Describe*
*Design*
*Develop*
*Discuss*
*Distinguish*
*Draw*
*Enumerate*
*Estimate*
*Evaluate*
*Experiment*
*Explain*
*Formulate*
*Generalize*
*Group*
*Identify*
*Infer*
*Interpret*
*Justify*
*Label*
*List*
*Make a claim*
*Measure*
*Model*
*Observe*
*Organize*
*Plan*
*Predict*
*Provide evidence*
*Reason*
*Record*
*Represent*
*Revise*
*Sequence*
*Solve*
*Sort*
*Strategize*
*Summarize*

**Constructing explanations (science) and designing solutions (engineering); engaging in argument from evidence**

- *Predict* future events, based on evidence and reasonings.
- Use data and logic to *construct* and *communicate* reasonable explanations.
- *Develop*, *discuss*, *evaluate*, and *justify* the merits of explanations.
- Use science-related technologies to *apply* scientific knowledge and *solve* problems.

**Developing and using models**

- Create models to *explain* natural phenomena and *predict* future events or outcomes.
- *Describe* how models represent the natural world.
- *Compare* models to actual phenomena and *identify* limitations of the models.

**Obtaining, evaluating, and communicating**

- *Identify* key ideas in text, identify supporting evidence, and know how to use various text features.
- *Distinguish* opinion from evidence.
- Use writing as a tool for *clarifying* ideas and *communicating*.

Research supports the claim that when students are intentionally using language functions in thinking about and communicating in science, they improve not only science content knowledge, but also language-arts and mathematics skills (Ostlund 1998; Lieberman and Hoody 1998). Language functions play a central role in science as a key cognitive tool for developing higher-order thinking and problem-solving abilities that, in turn, support academic literacy in all subject areas.

Here is an example of how an experienced teacher can provide an opportunity for students to exercise language functions in FOSS. In the **Soils, Rocks, and Landforms Module**, this is one piece of content we expect students to have acquired by the end of the module.

- The greater the flow of water across Earth's surface, the greater the rate of erosion and deposition.

The scientific practices the teacher wants the class to focus on are *interpreting data* and *constructing explanations*.

The language functions students will exercise while engaging in these scientific practices are *comparing, explaining*, and *providing evidence*. The teacher understands that these language functions are appropriate to the purpose of the science investigation and support the Common Core Standards for writing (students will write explanatory texts to examine a topic and convey ideas and information clearly).

- Students will *compare* observational data (from a stream–table investigation) to *explain* the relationship between the amount of water that runs over a surface and the amount of erosion and deposition that occur.

The teacher can support the use of language functions by providing structures such as sentence frames.

- As _____, then _____.

  *As more water flows over a surface, then more erosion and deposition occur.*

- When I changed _____, then _____ happened.

  *When I changed the amount of water flowing down the stream table, then more erosion and deposition happened.*

- The more/less _____, the _____.

  *The more water that flows across the earth materials, the more erosion and deposition that occur.*

▶ **NOTE**
For more examples of how FOSS teachers address language-arts standards while conducting science investigations with students, go to FOSSweb (www. FOSSweb.com).

## SPEAKING AND LISTENING DOMAIN

The FOSS investigations are designed to engage students in productive oral discourse. Talking requires students to process and organize what they are learning. Listening to and evaluating peers' ideas calls on students to apply their knowledge and to sharpen their reasoning skills. Guiding students in small-group and whole-class discussions is critical to the development of conceptual understanding of the science content and the ability to think and reason scientifically.

FOSS investigations start with a discussion—either a review to activate prior knowledge or presentation of a focus question or a challenge to motivate and engage active thinking. During active investigation, students talk with one another in small groups, share their observations and discoveries, point out connections, ask questions, and start to build explanations. The discussion icon in the sidebar of the *Investigations Guide* indicates when small-group discussions should take place.

During the activity, the *Investigations Guide* indicates where it is appropriate to pause for whole-class discussions to guide conceptual understanding. The *Investigations Guide* provides you with discussion questions to help stimulate student thinking and support sense making. At times, it may be beneficial to use sentence frames or standard prompts to scaffold the use of effective language functions and structures.

At the end of the investigation, there is another opportunity to develop language through speaking and listening in the Wrap-Up/Warm-Up. During this time, students are often asked to discuss their responses to the focus question. All students need to be engaged in this opportunity to use different language functions.

On the following pages are some suggestions for providing structure to those discussions and for scaffolding productive discourse when needed. Teaching techniques used to generate discussion in language arts and other content areas can also be used effectively during science. Using the protocols that follow will ensure inclusion of all students in discussions.

## Partner and Small-Group Discussion Protocols

Whenever possible, give students time to talk with a partner or in a small group before conducting a whole-class discussion. This provides all students with a chance to formulate their thinking, express their ideas, practice using the appropriate science vocabulary, and receive input from peers. Listening to others communicate different ways of thinking about the same information from a variety of perspectives helps students negotiate the difficult path of sense making for themselves.

**Dyads.** Students pair up and take turns either answering a question or expressing an idea. Each student has 1 minute to talk while the other student listens. While student A is talking, student B practices attentive listening. Student B makes eye contact with student A, but cannot respond verbally. After 1 minute, the roles reverse.

Here's an example from the **Mixtures and Solutions Module**. Just before students answer the focus question in their notebooks, you ask students to pair up and take turns sharing their answer to the question "How do you know when a chemical reaction has occurred?" The language objective is for students to be able to explain what happens during a chemical reaction and provide evidence (orally and in writing) that it has occurred. These sentence frames can be written on the board to scaffold student thinking and conversation.

- I claim that _____ produces a chemical reaction, because _____.

- Evidence for my claim includes _____.

**Partner parade.** Students form two lines facing each other. Present a question, an idea, an object, or an image as a prompt for students to discuss. Give students 1 minute to greet the person in front of them and discuss the prompt. After 1 minute, call time. Have the first student in one of the lines move to the end of the line, and have the rest of the students in that line shift one step sideways so that everyone has a new partner. (Students in the other line do not move.) Give students a new prompt to discuss for 1 minute with their new partners.

For example, students are just beginning the investigation on landforms, and you want to assess prior knowledge. Give each student a picture of a landform, and have students line up facing each other. For the first round, ask, "What do you know about the image on your card?" For the second round, ask, "How do you think the landform in your picture formed?" For the third round, ask, "What personal experience have you had with this landform?" The language objective is for students to describe their observations, infer how the landform formed,

**Partner and Small-Group Discussion Protocols**
- *Dyads*
- *Partner parade*
- *Put in your two cents*

and reflect upon and relate any experiences they may have had with a similar landform. The following sentence frames can be used to scaffold student discussion.

- I notice _____.

- I think the landform was formed by _____.

- The landform in my picture reminds me of the time when _____.

**Put in your two cents.** For small-group discussions, give each student two pennies or similar objects to use as talking tokens. Each student takes a turn putting a penny in the center of the table and sharing his or her idea. Once all have shared, each student takes a turn putting in the other penny and responding to what others in the group have said. For example,

- I agree (or don't agree) with _____ because _____.

Here's an example from the **Sun, Moon, and Planets Module**. Students have been monitoring their shadows throughout the day and are still struggling to make coherent connections between Earth's rotation and the effect that it has on shadows. The language objective is for students to describe their observations, explain why the direction and length of their shadows change during the day, and provide evidence based on their own observations. You give each student two pennies, and in groups of four, they take turns putting in their two cents. For the first round, each student answers the question "Why do shadows change during the day?" They use the frame

- I think shadows change during the day because _____.

- My evidence is _____ .

On the second round, each student states whether he or she agrees or disagrees with someone else in the group and why, using the sentence frame.

**Whole-Class Discussion Supports**
- *Sentence frames*
- *Guiding questions*

## Whole-Class Discussion Supports

The whole-class discussion is a critical part of sense making. After students have had the active learning experience and have talked with their peers in partners and/or small groups, sharing their observations with the whole class sets the stage for developing conventional explanatory models. Discrepant events, differing results, and other surprises are discussed, analyzed, and resolved. It is important that students realize that science is a process of finding out about the world around them. This is done through asking questions, testing ideas, forming explanations, and subjecting those explanations to logical scrutiny. Leading students through productive discussion helps them connect their observations and the abstract symbols (words) that represent and explain those observations. Whole-class discussion also provides an opportunity for you to interject an accurate and precise verbal summary statement as a model of the kind of thinking you are seeking. Facilitating effective whole-class discussions takes skill, practice, a shared set of norms, and patience. In the long run, students will have a better grasp of the content and improve their abilities to think independently and communicate effectively.

Norms should be established so that students know what is expected during science discussions.

- Science content and practices are the focus.

- Everyone participates.

- Ideas and experiences are shared, accepted, and valued. Everyone is respectful of one another.

- Claims are supported by evidence.

- Challenges (debate and argument) are part of the quest for complete understanding.

The same discussion techniques used during literacy circles and other whole-class discussions can be used during science instruction (e.g., attentive listening, staying focused on the speaker, asking questions, responding appropriately). In addition, in order for students to develop and practice their reasoning skills, they need to know the language forms and structures and the behaviors used in evidence-based debate and argument (e.g., using data to support claims, disagreeing respectfully, asking probing questions; Winokur and Worth 2006).

Explicitly model and conduct mini-lessons (5 to 10 minutes of focused instruction) on the language structures appropriate for active discussions, and provide time for students to practice them, using the science content.

**Sentence frames.** The following samples can be posted as a scaffold as students learn and practice their reasoning and oral participation skills.

- I think _____, because _____.

- I predict _____, because _____.

- I claim _____; my evidence is _____.

- I agree with _____ that _____.

- My idea is similar/related to _____'s idea.

- I learned/discovered/heard that _____.

- <Name> explained _____ to me.

- <Name> shared _____ with me.

- We decided/agreed that _____.

- Our group sees it differently, because _____.

- We have different observations/results. Some of us found that _____. One group member thinks that _____.

- We had a different approach/idea/solution/answer _____.

**Guiding questions.** The *Investigations Guide* provides questions to help concentrate student thinking on the concepts introduced in the investigation. Guiding questions should be used during the whole-class discussion to facilitate sense making. Here are some other open-ended questions that help guide student thinking and promote discussion.

- What did you notice when _____?

- What do you think will happen if _____?

- How might you explain _____? What is your evidence?

- What connections can you make between _____ and _____?

## Whole-Class Discussion Protocols

The following examples of tried-and-true participation protocols can be used to enhance whole-class discussions during science and all other curriculum areas. The purpose of these protocols is to increase meaningful participation by giving all students access to the discussion, allowing students time to think (process), and providing a context for motivation and engagement.

**Think-pair-share.** When asking for a response to a question posed to the class, allow time for students to think silently for a minute. Then, have students pair up with a partner to exchange thoughts before you call on a student to share his or her ideas with the whole class.

**Pick a stick.** Write each student's name on a craft stick, and keep the sticks handy at the front of the room. When asking for responses, randomly pick a stick, and call on that student to start the discussion. Continue to select sticks as you continue the discussion. Your name can also be on a stick in the cup. You can put the selected sticks in a different location or back into the same cup to be selected again.

**Whip around.** Each student takes a quick turn sharing a thought or reaction. Questions are phrased to elicit quick responses that can be expressed in one to five words (e.g., "Give an example of a stored-energy source." "What does the word *heat* make you think of?").

**Group posters.** Have small groups design and graphically record their investigation data and conclusions on a quickly generated poster to share with the whole class.

**Whole-Class Discussion Protocols**
- *Think-pair-share*
- *Pick a stick*
- *Whip around*
- *Group posters*

Two-cup pick-a-stick container

One-cup pick-a-stick container divided with tape

# WRITING DOMAIN

Information processing is enhanced when students engage in informal writing. When allowed to write expressively without fear of being scorned for incorrect spelling or grammar, students are more apt to organize and express their thoughts in different ways that support sense making. Writing promotes the use of scientific practices, thereby developing a deeper engagement with the science content. It also provides guidance for more formal derivative science writing (Keys 1999).

## Science Notebooks

The science notebook is an effective tool for enhancing learning in science and exercising various forms of writing. Science notebooks provide opportunities both for expressive writing (students craft explanatory narratives that make sense of their science experiences) and for practicing informal technical writing (students use organizational structures and writing conventions). Starting as emergent writers in kindergarten, students learn to communicate their thinking in an organized fashion while engaging in the cognitive processes required to develop concepts and build explanations. Having this developmental record of learning also provides an authentic means for assessing students' progress in both scientific thinking and communication skills.

One way to help students develop the writing skills necessary for productive notebook entries is to focus on the corresponding language functions. The language forms and structures used to perform these language functions in science are used in all curricular areas and, therefore, can be suitably taught in conjunction with existing language-arts instruction. This can be done through mini-lessons on the writing skills that support the various types of notebook entries.

Table 1, at the end of the Writing Domain section, provides examples of how language functions are used to help students develop both their general writing skills and their thinking abilities within the format of the science-notebook entry. The writing objectives for a mini-lesson, along with the particular language forms and structures (vocabulary, syntax, linking words, organization of ideas, and so on), are identified in the table along with the suggested sentence frames for scaffolding.

For example, if students are observing a particular insect's behavior, the language objective might be "Students describe in detail the behavior of the insect." A prior mini-lesson on using sensory details to describe observations would provide students with the language forms and structures appropriate for recording their data in their notebooks during the observations. As a scaffold, students could also be provided with sentence frames to help them write detailed narratives.

▶ **NOTE**
For more information about supporting science-notebook development, see the Science Notebooks chapter.

▶ **NOTE**
Language forms and structures refer to the internal grammatical structure of words and how those words go together to make sentences.

| Language function | Language objectives for writing in notebooks | Language forms, structures, and scaffolds for writing |
|---|---|---|
| **Notebook component—data acquisition** | | |
| Describe | Write narratives: use details, sensory observations, and connections to prior knowledge. | I observed ___. When I touch the ___, I feel ___. The ___ has ___. I noticed ___. It feels ___. It smells ___. It sounds ___. It reminds me of ___, because ___. |

This sample from Table 1 shows how language functions can be developed and applied when writing in science notebooks.

## Developing Derivative Language-Arts Products

Science notebooks provide students with a source of information (content) from which they can draw to create more formal science-centered writing pieces. Derivative products are written pieces that are generated with specific language-arts goals in mind, such as audience and language function. Writing-to-learn methods can enhance science concepts when students engage in different types of writing for different purposes (Hand and Prain 2002). We know that students are more engaged and motivated to write when they have a clear and authentic context for writing.

The language extensions in the Interdisciplinary Extensions section at the end of each investigation suggest writing activities that can be used to help students learn the science content for that particular investigation. The writing activities incorporate language-arts skills appropriate for the grade level. Questions and ideas for future writing activities that surface during the investigations can be recorded in a class list, in science notebooks, or in students' writing folders. Here are general suggestions for using science content to create products in each of several writing genres.

***Descriptive writing.*** Students use descriptive writing to portray an organism, an environment, an object, or a phenomenon in such a way that the reader can almost recapture the writer's experience. This is done through the use of sensory language; rich, vivid, and lively detail; and figurative language, such as simile, hyperbole, metaphor, and symbolism. You can remind students to show, rather than tell, through the use of active verbs and precise modifiers.

To help them learn the science content, students can use the information in their science notebooks to elaborate on their observations by using descriptive vocabulary, analogies, and drawing.

> **NOTE**
> The complete table appears at the end of this Writing Domain section.

**Derivative Language-Arts Products**
- *Descriptive writing*
- *Persuasive writing*
- *Narrative writing*
- *Expository writing*
- *Recursive cycle*

For example, kindergartners can draw pictures of isopods, fish, worms, things made of wood, different types of trees and leaves, and so on. Through drawings and words, students describe objects' properties and compare how those objects are the same and different.

Primary students can make property cards by writing on an index card as many properties as they can that describe an object or organism. Then, students take turns reading the properties to another student to see if the partner can identify the corresponding object.

Students of all ages can expand on their notebook entries in poetry that expresses their interpretation of organisms, objects, and phenomena such as crayfish, seeds, electricity, rivers, weather, and minerals. The use of similes is a good way to engage students in making comparisons. You can use a simple frame, such as: _____ is like _____. (For example, in the **Air and Weather Module**, students might write "The weather today is like a dragon.")

Students can share their similes. Other students can explain why they think the simile works.

***Persuasive writing.*** The objective of persuasive writing is to convince the reader that a stated opinion or interpretation of data is worthwhile and meaningful. Students learn to support their claims with evidence and to use persuasive techniques, such as logical arguments and calls to action. By using claims and evidence to formulate conclusions in their science notebooks, students develop and apply their thinking and reasoning skills to form the basis of persuasive writing in a variety of formats, such as essays, letters, editorials, advertisements, award nominations, informational pamphlets, and petitions. Animal habitats, energy use, weather patterns, landforms, and water sources are just a few science topics that can generate questions and issues for persuasive writing.

Here is a sample of persuasive writing frames (modified from Gibbons 2002).

> Title: _____
> The topic of this discussion is _____.
> My opinion (position, conclusion) is _____.
> There are <number> reasons why I believe this to be true.
> First, _____.
> Second, _____.
> Finally, _____.
> On the other hand, some people think _____.
> I have also heard people say _____.
> However, my claim is that _____ because _____.

**Narrative writing.** Science provides a broad landscape of engaging material for stimulating the imagination for the writing of stories, songs, biographies, autobiographies, poems, and plays. Students can use organisms or objects as characters; describe habitats and environments as settings; and write scripts portraying various systems, such as weather patterns, flow of electricity, and water, rock, or life cycles.

**Expository writing.** Students use science content to inform, explain, clarify, define, or instruct through writing letters, definitions, procedures, newspaper and magazine articles, posters, pamphlets, and research reports. Expository writing is characterized by a focus on main topics with supporting facts, details, explanations, and examples and is organized in a clear, coherent, and sequential manner. Expository writing has a clear focus on communicating accurate, complete, and detailed representations of science content and/or observation of natural history or events.

During writing instruction, students can use the information in their science notebooks and in related readings (and other sources, such as video content) to write a more formal and conclusive answer to the focus question. Strategies such as the writing process (plan, draft, edit, revise, and share) and writing frames (modeling and guiding the use of topic sentences, transition and sequencing words, examples, explanations, and conclusions) can be used with the science content to develop proficiency in critical writing skills.

> ▶ **NOTE**
> Human characteristics should not be given to organisms (anthropomorphism) in science investigations, only in literacy extensions.

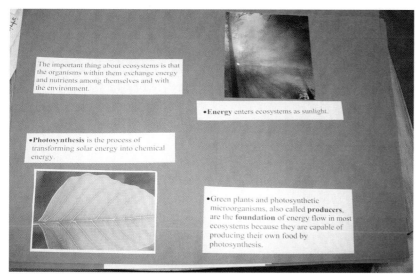

A page from a big book about ecosystems, a derivative product created during language arts

Here are three samples of writing frames for science reports for primary and upper-elementary students (modified from Wellington and Osborne 2001).

**Primary** (life cycle appropriate for the **Insects and Plants Module**)

Title: _____

(Define) A _____ is _____.

(Classify) A _____ is a kind of _____.

(Describe) A _____ is _____.

(Habitat) _____ lives _____.

(Life cycle) _____ started life as _____.

(Change over time) Then it _____.

(Food) A _____ eats _____.

(Evidence) I know that _____ because _____.

**Upper elementary** (living structures appropriate for the **Structures of Life Module**)

Title: _____

(Identify) The part of the body I am describing is the _____.

(Describe) It consists of _____.

(Explain) The function of these parts is _____.

(Example) This drawing shows _____.

**Upper elementary** (explanation)

Title: _____

I want to explain why (how) _____.

An important reason for why (how) this happens is that _____.

Another reason is that _____.

I know this because _____.

**Recursive cycle.** An effective method for extending students' science learning through writing is the recursive cycle of research (Bereiter 2002). This strategy emphasizes writing as a process for learning, similar to the way students learn during the active science investigations.

1. Decide on a problem or question to write about.

2. Formulate an idea or a conjecture about the problem or question.

3. Identify a remedy or an answer, and develop a coherent discussion.

4. Gather information (from science notebooks, *FOSS Science Resources*, books, FOSSweb interactives, Internet, interviews, videos, experiments, etc.).

5. Reevaluate the problem or question based on what has been learned.

6. Revise the idea or conjecture.

7. Make presentations (reports, posters, electronic presentations, etc.).

8. Identify new needs, and make new plans.

This process can continue for as long as new ideas and questions occur, or students can present a final product in any of the suggested formats.

Table 1. Examples of how language functions are exercised in science notebook writing and examples of sentence frames and language structures students may use

| Language function | Language objectives for writing in notebooks | Language forms, structures, and scaffolds for writing |
|---|---|---|
| **Organizational setup** | | |
| Organize | Set up and organize notebook: table of contents, glossary or index, page numbers, date, turning to the next blank page. | Use structures such as rows, columns, blocks, numbers, location, alphabetizing. |
| **Notebook component—planning the investigation** | | |
| Design Strategize | Write a narrative plan: communicate ideas on an approach to answer the focus question or challenge posed in the investigation. | Use adverbs such as *first, second, next, then, finally.* Brainstorming ideas: First I will ____, and then I will ____. I will need to ____ to ____. |
| List Record | Write ordered lists: materials, variables, vocabulary words, bullets | We need ____, ____, ____, and ____ to ____ . |
| Sequence | Record step-by-step procedures: explain exactly what to do, number steps in a sequence, specifics for measurement, how controls will be established, how variables will be measured (tools/units). | 1. _____.  2. _____.  3. _____.  I will change ____.  I will not change ____.  I will measure ____.  I will not measure ____. |
| **Notebook component—data acquisition** | | |
| Describe | Write narratives: use details, sensory observations, connections to prior knowledge. | I observed ____. When I touch the ____, I feel ____. The ____ has ____. I noticed ____. It feels ____. It smells ____. It sounds ____. It reminds me of ____, because ____. |

**Table 1 (*continued*)**

| Language function | Language objectives for writing in notebooks | Language forms, structures, and scaffolds for writing |
|---|---|---|
| **Notebook component—data acquisition** (continued) | | |
| Draw Label Identify | Make technical drawings: draw large, accurate, and detailed representations; identify parts of a system. | Label drawing, using science vocabulary. Recognize shapes, form, location, color, size, and scale. <br><br> My drawing shows ____. |
| Organize Compare Classify | Make charts and tables: use a T-table or chart for recording and displaying data. | Set up rows, columns, headings. <br><br> My T-table compares ____. |
| Sequence Compare | Record changes: use language structures to communicate change over time, cause and effect. | At first, ____, but now ____. We saw that first ____, then ____, and finally ____. When I ____, it ____. After I ____, it ____. |
| **Notebook component—data organization** | | |
| Enumerate | Plot graphs: decide when and how to use bar graphs, line plots, and two-coordinate graphs to organize data. | Define x- and y-axes; provide axis labels, title, units, coordinates; use equal intervals, set origin = (0, 0). |
| Compare Classify Sequence | Use graphic organizers and narratives to express similarities and differences, to assign an object or action to the category or type to which it belongs, and to show sequencing and order. | This ____ is the same as ____ because ____. This ____ is different than ____ because ____. All these are ____ because ____. ____, ____, and ____ all have/are ____. |
| Analyze | Use graphic organizers, narratives or concept maps to identify part/ whole or cause–and–effect relationships. | Use relationship verbs such as *contain*, *consist of*. As ____, then ____. When I changed ____, then ____ happened. The more/less ____, then ____. |

**Table 1** (*continued*)

| Language function | Language objectives for writing in notebooks | Language forms, structures, and scaffolds for writing |
|---|---|---|
| **Notebook component—making sense of data** | | |
| Infer<br>Explain | Provide claims and evidence: write assertions about what was learned from the investigation, use the data as evidence to support those claims. | Use inferential logical connectors such as *although*, *while*, *thus*, *therefore*.<br>I claim that ____. I know this because ____. |
| Provide evidence | Use qualitative and quantitative data from the investigation as evidence to support claims. | Use qualitative descriptors such as *more/less*, *longer/shorter*, *brighter/dimmer*. Use quantitative expressions using standard metric units of measurement such as cm, mL, °C.<br>My data show ____. |
| Summarize<br>Predict<br>Generalize | Write a summary narrative to communicate what was learned; ask questions and make predictions based on the newly acquired knowledge. | Answer the focus question by rewriting it as a statement and providing evidence from data. Make a concluding statement. I learned ____. Therefore, I think ____. I predict ____ because ____.<br>A new question I have is ____. |
| **Notebook component—next-step strategies** | | |
| Critique<br>Evaluate | Reflect on experience: review notebook entries and revise, using line of learning or 3 Cs (correct in red, confirm in green, and complete in blue). | I used to think ____, but now I think ____. I have changed my thinking about ____.<br>I am confused about ____ because ____. I wonder ____. |

# READING DOMAIN

Reading is an integral part of science learning. Just as scientists spend a significant amount of their time reading one another's published works, students need to learn to read scientific text—to read effectively for understanding with a critical focus on the ideas being presented.

The articles in *FOSS Science Resources* help facilitate sense making as students make connections to the science concepts introduced and explored during the active investigations. Concept development is most effective when students are allowed to experience organisms, objects, and phenomena firsthand before engaging the concepts in text. The text and illustrations help students make connections between what they have experienced concretely and the abstract ideas that explain their observations.

*FOSS Science Resources* supports developing literacy skills by providing reading material that corresponds exactly to the concrete, personal experience provided in the active investigations. Students read with enthusiasm when they recognize familiar materials, organisms, and activities and are eager to tackle the reading to confirm their prior knowledge and discover more about the topic. In addition to making connections, once engaged, students naturally use other reading-comprehension strategies, such as asking questions, visualizing, inferring, and synthesizing, to help them understand the reading. As students apply these strategies, they are, in effect, using some of the same scientific thinking processes that promote critical thinking and problem solving.

## Reading in the Primary Grades

In the kindergarten modules, you can enhance science learning by using trade books and other read-aloud resources to engage students and provide topics for lively discussions. Reading aloud helps primary students understand the science content and lets you model reading-comprehension strategies, such as asking yourself questions (thinking aloud) and summarizing a paragraph just read. The Reading in *FOSS Science Resources* sections (in every part that has a reading) usually offer suggestions for activating prior knowledge before reading, indicate places to pause and discuss key points during the reading, and describe activities to deepen understanding after the reading. As students develop their reading skills, you might try these different ways to read from *FOSS Science Resources*.

- Read aloud from the big book while students follow along in their own books.

- Lead students in small guided reading groups.

- Have students read aloud with a partner.

- Have students read silently on their own.

The same strategies used in language arts can be applied to reading in science. Begin with reading the article aloud so that students can hear the content read fluently and listen for meaning and coherence. Go back and review the questions within the article. Use think-pair-share or other discussion protocols to allow students to think first, share with a partner, and then respond to the group. Emphasize blending phonemes as you read the text again, and model tracking, connecting spoken words with written words, and helping students identify sight words. Model reading-comprehension strategies by using think-alouds (as you think aloud, you explain the process that you are using in order to understand the text while reading). The expository text structure also provides the opportunity for primary students to learn how to extract information from a table of contents, a glossary, an index, and other text conventions such as headings, subheads, boldface and italic print, labeled graphics, and captions.

At the end of articles, use the questions provided to guide understanding and to assess comprehension and vocabulary acquisition. Choose one or two questions for students to answer in their notebooks. Emphasize the importance of science vocabulary and the appropriate language forms and structures. Here are some ways students can enhance reading comprehension.

- Have students predict the sequence of events or content.

- Have students write or dictate questions about the text and illustrations.

- Use visualization with students to "see, touch, feel, smell, hear" in their minds the content presented in the article.

- Ask students to make connections to information in the article and their observations during the active investigation.

## Reading in the Upper-Elementary Grades

As students progress from *learning to read* to *reading to learn*, they apply the strategies and skills of reading comprehension to learning about science in *FOSS Science Resources* and other texts. Writing becomes increasingly important in helping students make sense of the readings as well as the active investigations. Use the suggested questions in the *Investigations Guide* to support comprehension as students read from *FOSS Science Resources*. For most of the investigation parts, the articles are designed to follow the active investigation and are interspersed throughout the flow of the module. This allows students to acquire the necessary background knowledge through active experience before tackling the wider-ranging content and relationships presented in the text. Additional strategies for reading are derived from the seven essential strategies that readers use to help them understand what they read (Keene and Zimmermann 2007).

- Monitor for meaning: Discover when you know and when you don't know.

- Use and create schemata: Make connections between the novel and the known; activate and apply background knowledge.

- Ask questions: Generate questions before, during, and after reading that reach for deeper engagement with the text.

- Determine importance: Decide what matters most, what is worth remembering.

- Infer: Combine background knowledge with information from the text to predict, conclude, make judgments, and interpret.

- Use sensory and emotional images: Create mental images to deepen and stretch meaning.

- Synthesize: Create an evolution of meaning by combining understanding with knowledge from other texts/sources.

Following are some strategies that enhance the reading of expository texts in general and have proven to be particularly helpful in science.

***Build on background knowledge.*** Activating prior knowledge is critical for helping students make connections between what they already know and new information. Reading comprehension improves when students have the opportunity to think, discuss, and write about what they know about a topic before reading. Review what students learned from the active investigation, provide prompts for making connections, and ask questions to help students recall past experiences and previous exposure to concepts related to the reading.

### Strategies for Reading in Upper-Elementary Grades
- *Build on background knowledge*
- *Create an anticipation guide*
- *Draw attention to vocabulary*
- *Preview the text*
- *Turn and talk*
- *Jigsaw text reading*
- *Note making*
- *Interactive reading aloud*
- *Summarize and synthesize*
- *3-2-1*
- *Write reflections*
- *Preview and predict*
- *SQ3R*

**Create an anticipation guide.** Create true-or-false statements related to the key ideas in the reading selection. Ask students to indicate if they agree or disagree with each statement before reading, then have them read the text, looking for the information that supports their true-or-false claims. Anticipation guides connect students to prior knowledge, engage them with the topic, and encourage them to explore their own thinking.

**Draw attention to vocabulary.** Check the article for bold words to determine if there are words students may not know. Review the science words that have already been listed on the word wall and in students' notebooks. For new science and nonscience vocabulary words that appear in the reading, have students predict their meanings before reading. During the reading, have students use strategies such as context clues and word structure to see if their predictions were correct. This strategy activates prior knowledge and engages students by encouraging analytical participation with the text.

**Preview the text.** Give students time to skim through the selection, noting subheads, before reading thoroughly. Point out the particular structure of the text and what discourse markers to look for. For example, most *FOSS Science Resources* articles are written as cause and effect, problem and solution, question and answer, comparison and contrast, description, and sequence. Students will have an easier time making sense of the text if they know what to look for in terms of text structure. Model and have students practice analyzing these different types of expository text structures by looking for examples, patterns, and the discourse markers.

Point out how *FOSS Science Resources* text is organized (titles, headings, subheadings, questions, and summaries) and how to use the table of contents, glossary, and index. Explain how to scan for formatting features that provide key information (such as bold type and italics, captions, and framed text) and graphic features (such as tables, graphs, photographs, maps, diagrams, charts, and illustrations) that help clarify, elaborate, and explain important information in the reading.

While students preview the article, have them focus on the questions that appear in the text, as well as questions at the end of the article. Encourage students to write down questions they have that they think the reading will answer.

▶ **NOTE**
Discourse markers are words or phrases that relate one idea to another. Examples are "however," "on the other hand," and "second."

**Turn and talk.** When reading as a whole class, stop at key points and have students share their thinking about the selection with the student sitting next to them or in their collaborative group. This strategy helps students process the information and allows everyone to participate in the discussion. When reading in pairs, encourage students to stop and discuss with their partners. One way to encourage engagement and understanding during paired reading is to have students take turns reading aloud a paragraph or section on a certain topic. The one who is listening then summarizes the meaning conveyed in the passage.

**Jigsaw text reading.** Students work together in small groups (expert teams) to develop a collective understanding of a text. Each expert team is responsible for one portion of the assigned text. The teams read and discuss their portions to gain a solid understanding of the key concepts. They might use graphic organizers to refine and organize the information. Each expert team then presents its piece to the rest of the class. Or new, small jigsaw groups can be formed that consist of at least one representative from each expert team. Each student shares with the jigsaw group what their team learned from their particular portion of the text. Together, the participants in the jigsaw group fit their individual pieces together to create a complete picture of the content in the article.

**Note making.** The more interactive that students make a reading, the better for their understanding. Encourage students to become active readers by asking them to make notes as they read. Studies have shown that note making—especially paraphrasing and summarizing—is one of the most effective means for understanding text (Graham and Herbert 2010; Applebee 1984).

Students can annotate the text by writing thoughts and questions on self-stick notes. Using symbols or codes can help facilitate comprehension monitoring. Here are some possible symbols (Harvey 1998).

| | |
|---|---|
| ★ | interesting |
| BK | background knowledge |
| ? | question |
| C | confusing |
| I | important |
| L | learning something new |
| W | wondering |
| S | surprising |

**An example of annotated text in *FOSS Science Resources***

Students can use a set of symbols while making notes about connections. The readings in *FOSS Science Resources* incorporate the active learning that students gain from the investigations so that they can make authentic text-to-self (T-S) connections. In other words, what they read reminds them of firsthand experiences, making the article more engaging and easier to understand. Text-to-text (T-T) connections are notes students make when they discover a new idea that reminds them of something they've read previously in another text. Text-to-world (T-W) connections involve the text and more global everyday connections to students' lives.

You can model note-making strategies by displaying a selection of text, using a projection system, a document camera, or an interactive whiteboard. As you read the text aloud, model how to write comments on self-stick notes, and use a graphic organizer in a notebook to enhance understanding.

Graphic organizers help students focus on extracting the important information from the reading and analyzing relationships between concepts. This can be done by simply having students make columns in their notebooks to record information and their thinking (Harvey and Goudvis 2007). Here are two examples of graphic organizers.

| Notes | Thinking |
|-------|----------|
|       |          |

| Facts | Questions | Responses |
|-------|-----------|-----------|
|       |           |           |

**Interactive reading aloud.** Reading aloud is an effective strategy for enhancing text comprehension. It offers opportunities to model specific reading-comprehension strategies and allows students to concentrate on making sense of the content. When modeling, share the thinking processes used to understand the reading (questioning, visualizing, comparing, inferring, summarizing, etc.), then have students share what they observed you thinking about as an active reader.

**Summarize and synthesize.** Model how to pick out the important parts of the reading selection. Paraphrasing is one way to summarize. Have students record summaries of the reading, using their own words. To scaffold the learning, use graphic organizers to compare and contrast, group, sequence, and show cause and effect. Another method is to have students make two columns in their notebooks. In one column, they record what is important, and in the other they record their personal responses (what the reading makes them think about). When writing summaries, tell students,

- *Pick out the important ideas.*

- *Restate the main ideas in your own words.*

- *Keep it brief.*

**3-2-1.** This strategy gives students the opportunity to synthesize information and formulate questions they still have regarding the concepts covered in an article. In their notebooks, students write three new things they learned, two interesting things worth remembering and sharing, and one question that occurred to them while reading the article. Other options might include three facts, two interesting ideas, and one insight about themselves as learners; three key words, two new ideas, and one thing to think about (modified from Black Hills Special Service Cooperative 2006).

**Write reflections.** After reading, ask students to review their notes in their notebooks to make any additions, revisions, or corrections to what they recorded during the reading. This review can be facilitated by using a line of learning. Students draw a line under their original conclusion or under their answer to a question posed at the end of an article. They then add any new information as a new narrative entry. The line of learning indicates that what follows represents a change of thinking.

**Preview and predict.** Instruct students to independently preview the article, directing attention to the illustrations, photos, boldfaced words, captions, and anything else that draws their attention. Working with a partner, students discuss and write three things they think they will learn from the article. Have partners verbally share their list with another pair of students. The group of four can collaborate to generate one list. Teams report their ideas, and together you create a class list on chart paper.

Read the article aloud, or have students read with a partner aloud or silently. Referring to the preview/prediction list, discuss what students learned. Have them record the most important thing they learned from the reading for comparison with the predictions.

**SQ3R.** Survey! Question! Read! Recite! Review! provides an overall structure for before, during, and after reading. Students begin by previewing the text, looking for features that will help them make predictions about content. Based on their surveys, students develop questions to answer as they read. Students then read the selection. They recite by telling a partner what they've learned (their partner listens carefully to their recitation, making sure they haven't missed any important concepts) and answering any questions their partner might have. Finally, they review their questions and answers. There is value in asking students to make their entire SQ3R process explicit.

Use this script as an outline, using appropriate wording where necessary.

**Survey! Question!**

a. Before you read, survey (preview) the reading selection.

b. As you survey, think of questions that the reading might answer while you read the title, headings, and subheadings.

c. Read the questions at the end of the article.

d. Ask yourself, "What did my teacher say about this selection when it was assigned?"

e. Ask yourself, "What do I already know about this subject from experiments or discussions we've had in class?"

## Read!

a. While reading, look for answers to the questions you raised.

b. Think about answers for the questions at the end of the article.

c. Study graphics, such as pictures, graphs, and tables.

d. Reread captions associated with pictures, graphs, and tables.

e. Note all italicized and boldfaced words or phrases.

f. Reduce your reading speed for difficult passages.

g. Stop and reread parts that are not clear.

h. Read only a section at a time, and recite after each section.

## Recite!

a. After you've read a section, make notes in your science notebook by writing information in your own words.

b. Underline or highlight important notes in your science notebook.

c. Use the method of recitation that best suits your particular learning style. Remember that the more senses you use, the more likely you are to remember what you read. Seeing, saying, hearing, and writing will all enhance learning.

d. Ask questions aloud about what you just read, and summarize aloud, in your own words, what you read.

e. Listen attentively as your partner recites.

## Review!

Reviewing should be ongoing. With the whole class, review the entire process, calling on groups to talk to the class about what they've learned.

## Struggling Readers

For students reading below grade level, the strategies listed above can be modified to support reading comprehension by integrating strategies from the Reading in the Primary Grades section, such as read-alouds and guided reading. Students can also follow along with the audio stories on FOSSweb. Breaking the reading down into smaller chunks, providing graphic organizers, and modeling reading-comprehension strategies can also help students who may be struggling with the text. For additional strategies for English learners, see the supported-reading strategy in the English-Language Development section of this chapter.

## SCIENCE-VOCABULARY DEVELOPMENT

Words play two critically important functions in science. First and most important, we play with ideas in our minds, using words. We present ourselves with propositions—possibilities, questions, potential relationships, implications for action, and so on. The process of sorting out these thoughts involves a lot of internal conversation, internal argument, weighing of options, and complex linguistic decisions. Once our minds are made up, communicating that decision, conclusion, or explanation in writing or through verbal discourse requires the same command of the vocabulary. Words represent intelligence; acquiring the precise vocabulary and the associated meanings is key to successful scientific thinking and communication.

The words introduced in FOSS investigations represent or relate to fundamental science concepts and should be taught in the context of the investigation. Many of the terms are abstract and are critical to developing science content knowledge and scientific and engineering practices. The goal is for students to use science vocabulary in ways that demonstrate understanding of the concepts the words represent—not to merely recite scripted definitions. The most effective science-vocabulary development strategies help students make connections to what they already know. These strategies focus on giving new words conceptual meaning through experience; distinguishing between informal, everyday language and academic language; and using the words in meaningful contexts.

### Building Conceptual Meaning through Experience

In most instances, students should be presented with new words in the context of the active experience at the need-to-know point in the investigation. Words such as *flexible, magnetic, viscous, silt, erode,* and *electricity* are conceptually loaded and significantly abstract. Students will have a much better chance of understanding, assimilating, and remembering the new word (or new meaning) if they can connect it with a concrete experience.

The new-word icon appears in the sidebar when you introduce a word that is critical to understanding the concepts or scientific practices students will be learning and applying in the investigation. When you introduce a new word, students should

- Hear it: Students listen as you model the correct contextual use and pronunciation of the word.

- See it: Students see the new word written out. Add a visual reference (an illustration or a sample) next to the word if possible.

- Say it: Have primary-grade students repeat the word chorally and clap out the syllables.

- Write it: You write the word on the board, chart paper, sentence strip, or card. Students use the new words in context when they write in their notebooks.

- Act it: Demonstrate action words such as *separate*, *compare*, and *observe* (using total physical response).

## Bridging Informal Language to Science Vocabulary

Students bring a wealth of language experience to the classroom. FOSS investigations are designed to tap into students' inquisitive natures and their excitement of discovery in order to encourage lively discussions as they explore materials in creative ways. There should be a lot of talking during science time! Your role is to help students connect informal language to the vocabulary used to express specific science concepts. As you circulate during active investigation, you continually model the use of science vocabulary. For example, when a student holds up a bottle of water and says, "I can see through it!" you might respond, "Yes, I see what you mean; the liquid in the bottle is transparent." Following are some strategies for validating students' conversational language while developing their familiarity with and appreciation for science vocabulary.

**Word bubbles.** Choose a word from the word wall that is widely used by students and that is a synonym for a science vocabulary word. Draw a circle on the board or chart paper, and write the word in the center. Draw lines out from the circled word, and make more circles. Ask students to call out more synonyms for the word, and write them in the outer circles. Introduce the target vocabulary word as yet one more synonym for the target word, a word that is used in science. Highlight the word, and model its correct usage and pronunciation. Encourage students to use it in their discussions and in their notebook entries. Introduce the science word that is its opposite, when appropriate.

**Bridging Language Strategies**
- *Word bubbles*
- *Word sorts*
- *Semantic webs*
- *Concept maps*
- *Cognitive content dictionaries*
- *Word associations*

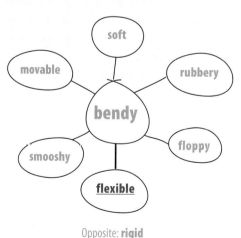

Opposite: **rigid**

**Word bubbles**

**Word sorts.** Make a set of word cards from words on the word wall. Ask students to help you group the words that are synonyms or that have conceptual connections. Add the new science words to the card set. Repeat the process with a new set of words. For upper-elementary students, make sets of vocabulary cards for students to sort in small groups.

**Semantic webs.** Select a vocabulary word, and write it in the center of a piece of paper (or on the board if doing this with the whole class). Brainstorm a list of words or ideas that are related to the first word. Group the words and concepts into several categories, and attach them to the central word with lines, forming a web (modified from Hamilton 2002).

**Concept maps.** Select six to ten related science words. Have students write them on self-stick notes or cards. Have small groups discuss how the words/concepts are related. Students organize words in groups and glue them down or copy them onto a sheet of paper. Students draw lines between the related words. On the lines, they write words describing or explaining how the concept words are related.

**Cognitive content dictionaries.** There are many variations of frameworks to help students record new words. This example can be used with the whole class with primary students or individually with upper-elementary students to introduce a few key vocabulary words used in an investigation. Have students write the word, predict its meaning, write the final meaning after class discussion (using primary language or an illustration when appropriate), and then use the word in a sentence. The word can then be used as a signal word to call for attention.

| Cognitive Content Dictionary | |
| --- | --- |
| New word | esker |
| Prediction (clues) | a flower growing at the North Pole |
| Final meaning (e.g., primary language, pictures) | a sand and gravel ridge, formed at the edges of a stream, flowing under a glacier |
| How I would use it (sentence) | The esker showed that a glacier had been in the valley at some time in the past. |

**Word associations.** In this brainstorming activity, you say a word, and students respond by writing the first word that comes to mind. Then students share their words with the class. This activity builds connections to students' prior frames of deference.

# Using Science Vocabulary in Context

In order for a new vocabulary word to become part of a student's functional vocabulary, he or she must have ample opportunities to hear and use it. The use of vocabulary terms is embedded in the activities through teacher talk, whole-class and small-group discussions during investigations, writing in science notebooks, readings, assessments, and games. In addition, other methods used during language-arts instruction can be used to reinforce important vocabulary words and phrases.

**Word wall/word cards.** Use chart paper or a pocket chart to record both science content and procedural words. Record the words as they come up during and after the investigations. Then copy key words on sentence strips or cards, and put them in a pocket chart. With a pocket chart, words can be sorted and moved around easily. For example, you could ask students to find words that are synonyms, antonyms, nouns, or verbs. Word cards should be available to each group during the investigation. This allows students to retrieve a word quickly when they are labeling diagrams and objects used during the investigation.

**Drawings and diagrams.** For English learners and visual learners, a diagram can be used to review and explain abstract content. Ahead of time, draw an illustration lightly, almost invisibly, with pencil on chart paper. When it's time for the investigation, trace the illustration with markers as you introduce the words and phrases to students. Students will be amazed by your artistic ability.

**Cloze activities.** Structure a sentence for students to complete, leaving out the vocabulary word, and crafting the sentence so that the missing vocabulary word is the last word in the sentence. You can do this chorally with primary students or in writing on the board or chart paper for upper-elementary students. Here's an example from the **Solids and Liquids Module**.

> Teacher: *Liquids that are clear and that you can see through are _____.*
>
> Students: *Transparent.*

## Science Vocabulary Strategies
- *Word wall/word cards*
- *Drawings and diagrams*
- *Cloze activities*
- *Word wizard*
- *Word analysis/word parts*
- *Breaking apart words*
- *Possible sentences*
- *Reading*
- *Highlighting the vocabulary*
- *Index*
- *Poems, chants, and songs*
- *Games*

**Word wizard.** Tell students that you are going to lead a word activity. You will be thinking of a science vocabulary word from the word wall. The goal is to figure out the word. Provide hints that have to do with parts of a definition, root word, prefix, suffix, and other relevant components. Students work in teams of two to four. Provide one hint, and give teams 1 minute to discuss. One team member writes the word on a piece of paper or on the whiteboard, using dark marking pens. Each team holds up its word for only you to see. After the third clue, reveal the word, and move on to the next word.

1. *This word is part of a plant.*

2. *It is usually not green.*

3. *It brings water and nutrients into the plant.*

*It is the* **root**.

**Word analysis/word parts.** Learning clusters of words that share a common origin can help students understand content-area texts and connect new words to familiar ones. This type of contextualized teaching meets the immediate need of understanding an unknown word while building generative knowledge that supports students in figuring out difficult words for future reading.

*geology*

*geologist*

*geological*

*geography*

*geometry*

*geophysical*

**Breaking apart words.** Have teams of two to four students break the word into prefix, root word, and suffix. Give each team different words, and have each team share the parsed elements of the word with the whole class.

**electromagnetism**

*electro*: having to do with electricity

*magnet*: having polar properties; attraction and repulsion of opposite and similar poles

*ism*: relating to a theory of how things behave

**Possible sentences.** Here is a simple strategy for teaching word meanings and generating class discussion.

1. Choose six to eight key concept words from the text of an article in *FOSS Science Resources*.

2. Choose four to six additional words that students are more likely to know something about.

3. Put the list of 10–14 words on the board or project it. Provide brief definitions as needed.

4. Ask students to devise sentences that include two or more words from the list.

5. On chart paper, write all sentences that students generate, both coherent and otherwise.

6. Have students read the article from which the words were extracted.

7. Revisit students' sentences, and discuss whether the sentences are sensible based on the passage or how they could be modified to be more coherent.

**Reading.** After the active investigation, students continue to develop their understanding of the vocabulary words and the concepts those words represent by listening to you read aloud, reading with a partner, or reading independently. Use strategies discussed in the Reading Domain section to encourage students to articulate their thoughts and practice the new vocabulary.

**Highlighting the vocabulary.** Emphasize the vocabulary words students should be using when they answer the focus question in their science notebooks. Distribute copies of the vocabulary/glossary for the investigation (available on FOSSweb) for students to glue into their notebooks. As you introduce the words in the investigation, students highlight them.

**Index.** Have students create an index at the back of their notebooks. There, they can record new vocabulary words and the notebook page where they defined and used the new words for the first time in the context of the investigation.

**Poems, chants, and songs.** Vocabulary words and phrases can be reinforced using content-rich poems, rhymes, chants, and songs.

**Games.** The informal activities included in the investigations are designed to reinforce important vocabulary words. Once students learn them, the words can be integrated into any type of independent work time, such as centers, workshops, and early-finisher tasks.

▶ **NOTE**
See the Science Notebooks in Grades 3–6 chapter for an example of this index.

▶ **NOTE**

English-language development refers to the advancement of students' ability to read, write, and speak English.

### EL NOTE

*Look for EL Notes in the investigations at points where students at beginning levels of English proficiency may need additional support.*

## ENGLISH-LANGUAGE DEVELOPMENT

Active investigations, together with ample opportunities to develop and use language, provide an optimal learning environment for English learners. This section highlights the English-language development (ELD) opportunities inherent in FOSS investigations and suggests other best practices for facilitating both the learning of new science concepts and the development of academic vocabulary and language structures that enhance literacy. For example, the hands–on structure of FOSS investigations is essential for the conceptual development of science content knowledge and the habits of mind that guide and define scientific practices. Students are engaged in concrete experiences that are meaningful and that provide a shared context for developing understanding—critical components for ELD instruction.

To further address the needs of English learners, the *Investigations Guide* includes EL Notes at points in the investigations where students at beginning levels of English proficiency may need additional support. When getting ready for an investigation, review the EL Notes, and determine the points where English learners may require scaffolds and where the whole class might benefit from additional language-development supports. One way to plan for ELD integration in science is to keep in mind four key areas: prior knowledge, comprehensible input, academic language development, and oral practice. The ELD chart below lists examples of universal strategies for each of these components that work particularly well in teaching science.

| English-Language Development (ELD) Quadrants | |
|---|---|
| **Activating prior knowledge**<br>• Inquiry chart<br>• Circle map<br>• Observation poster<br>• Quick write<br>• Kit inventory | **Using comprehensible input**<br>• Content objectives<br>• Multiple exposures<br>• Visual aids<br>• Supported reading<br>• Procedural vocabulary |
| **Developing academic language**<br>• Language objectives<br>• Sentence frames<br>• Word wall, word cards, drawings<br>• Concept maps<br>• Cognitive content dictionaries | **Providing oral practice**<br>• Small-group discussions<br>• Science talk<br>• Oral presentations<br>• Poems, chants, and songs<br>• Teacher feedback |

# Activating Prior Knowledge

When an investigation engages a new concept, first students recall and discuss familiar situations, objects, or experiences that relate to and establish a foundation for building new knowledge and conceptual understanding. Eliciting prior knowledge also supports learning by motivating interest, acknowledging culture and values, and checking for misconceptions and prerequisite knowledge. This is usually done in the first steps of Guiding the Investigation in the form of an oral discussion, presentation of new materials, or a written response to a prompt. The tools outlined below can also be used before beginning an investigation to establish a familiar context for launching into new material.

**Circle maps.** Draw two concentric circles on chart paper. In the middle circle, write the topic to be explored. In the second circle, record what students already know about the subject. Ask students to think about how they know or learned what they already know about the topic. Record the responses outside the circles. Students can also do this independently in their science notebooks.

**An example of a circle map**

**Strategies for Activating Prior Knowledge**
- *Circle maps*
- *Observation posters*
- *Quick writes*
- *Kit inventories*

# Science-Centered Language Development

**Observation posters.** Make observation posters by gluing or taping pictures and artifacts relevant to the module or a particular investigation onto pieces of blank chart paper or poster paper. Hang them on the walls in the classroom, and have students rotate in small groups to each poster. At each station, students discuss their observations with their partners or small groups and then record (write, draw, or dictate) an observation, a question, a prediction, or an inference about the pictures as a contribution to the commentary on the poster.

An observation poster

**Quick writes.** Ask students what they think they know about the topic of the investigation. Responses can be recorded independently as a quick write in science notebooks and then shared collaboratively. You should not correct misconceptions initially. Periodically revisit the quick-write ideas as a whole class, or have students review their notebook entries to correct, confirm, or complete their original thoughts as new information is acquired (possibly using a line of learning). At the conclusion of the investigation, students should be able to express mastery of the new conceptual material.

**Kit inventories.** Introduce each item from the FOSS kit used in the investigation, and ask students questions to get them thinking about what each item is and where they may have seen it before. Have them describe the objects and make predictions about how they will be used in the investigation. Tape samples of the items on chart paper, or print and display the equipment photo cards (download from FOSSweb) along with the name and a description, to serve as an interactive word wall.

Wood cylinder

| Item | Teacher | Student |
|---|---|---|
| Bottle | What is this? | A bottle. |
| | What is it made of? | Plastic. |
| | What is it used for? | To hold liquids. |
| Scoop | What is this? | It looks like a spoon. |
| | It's like a spoon. It's called a scoop. | Like an ice-cream scoop! |
| | What do you think we will be using it for in science? | To scoop things up. |
| Funnel | Have you seen this before? | My mom uses that for the car. |
| | It's called a funnel. Where else have you seen this? | In the kitchen. My uncle uses it sometimes to pour things. |
| | Can you describe it? | It's round on the ends. It's bigger on one end, and it's hollow. |
| Beaker | Have you seen this before? | We used it for science last year to measure and pour water. |
| | It's called a beaker. Where else have you seen this? | |
| Vial | This is a vial. What do you think we will be using it for in science? | To hold small things. |

**A kit inventory script from the Solids and Liquids Module**

# Comprehensible Input

In order to initiate their own sense-making process, students must be able to access the information presented to them. We refer to this ability as comprehensible input. Students must understand the essence of new ideas and concepts before beginning the process of constructing new scientific meaning. The strategies for comprehensible input used in FOSS ensure that the delivery of instruction is understandable while providing students with the opportunity to grapple with new ideas and the critically important relationships between concepts. Additional tools such as repetition, visual aids, emphasis on procedural vocabulary, and auditory reinforcement can also be used to enhance comprehensible input for English learners.

**Content objectives.** The focus question for each investigation part frames the activity objectives—what students should know or be able to do at the end of the part. Making the learning objectives clear and explicit helps English learners prepare to process the delivery of new information, and helps you maintain the focus of the investigation. Write the focus question on the board, have students read it aloud and transcribe it into their science notebooks, and have students answer the focus question at the end of the investigation part. You then check their responses for understanding.

### Strategies for Comprehensible Input
- *Content objectives*
- *Multiple exposures*
- *Visual aids*
- *Supported reading*
- *Procedural vocabulary*

# Science-Centered Language Development

**Procedural Vocabulary**

Add
Analyze
Assemble
Attach
Calculate
Change
Classify
Collect
Communicate
Compare
Connect
Construct
Contrast
Describe
Demonstrate
Determine
Draw
Evaluate
Examine
Explain
Explore
Fill
Graph
Identify
Illustrate
Immerse
Investigate
Label
List
Measure
Mix
Observe
Open
Order
Organize
Pour
Predict
Prepare
Record
Represent
Scratch
Separate
Sort
Stir
Subtract
Summarize
Test
Weigh

**Multiple exposures.** Repeat the activity as a class, at a center during independent work time, or in an analogous but slightly different context, ideally one that incorporates elements that are culturally relevant to students.

**Visual aids.** On the board or chart paper, write out the steps for conducting the investigation. This will provide a visual reference. Include illustrations if necessary. Use graphic representations (illustrations drawn and labeled in front of students) to review the concepts explored in the active investigations. In addition to the concrete objects included in the kit, use realia to augment the activity to help English learners build understanding and make cultural connections. Graphic organizers (webs, Venn diagrams, T-tables, flowcharts, etc.) aid comprehension by helping students see how ideas (concepts) are related.

**Supported reading.** In addition to the reading comprehension strategies suggested in the Reading Domain section of this chapter, English learners can also benefit from methods such as front-loading key words, phrases, and complex text structures before reading; using preview-review (main ideas are previewed in the primary language, read in English, and reviewed in the primary language); and having students use sentence frames specifically tailored to record key information and/or graphic organizers that make the content and the relationship between concepts visually explicit from the text as they read.

**Procedural vocabulary.** Make sure students understand the meaning of the words used in the directions describing what they should be doing during the investigation. These may or may not be science-specific words. Use techniques such as modeling, demonstrating, and body language (gestures) to explain procedural meaning in the context of the investigation. The words students will encounter in FOSS include those listed in the sidebar. To build academic literacy, English learners need to learn the multiple meanings of these words and their specific meanings in the context of science.

## Developing Academic Language

As students learn the nuances of the English language, it is critical that they build proficiency in academic language in order to participate fully in the cognitive demands of school. Academic language refers to the more abstract, complex, and specific aspects of language, such as the words, grammatical structure, and discourse markers that are needed for higher cognitive learning. FOSS investigations introduce and provide opportunities for students to practice using the academic vocabulary needed to access and meaningfully engage with science ideas.

**Language objectives.** Consider the language needs of English learners and incorporate specific language-development objectives that will support learning the science content of the investigation, such as a specific word knowledge skill (a way to expand use of vocabulary by looking at root words, prefixes, and suffixes), a linguistic pattern or structure for oral discussion and writing, or a reading-comprehension strategy. Recording in students' science notebooks is a productive place to optimize science learning and language objectives. For example, in the **Pebbles, Sand, and Silt Module**, one language objective might be "Students will describe what happened when they rubbed their rocks together (think-pair-share) and answer the focus question in their notebooks, using a cause–and–effect sentence frame."

**Vocabulary development.** The Science-Vocabulary Development section in this chapter describes the ways science vocabulary is introduced and developed in the context of an active investigation and suggests methods and strategies that can be used to support vocabulary development during instruction in English language arts and ELD. In addition to science vocabulary, students also need to learn the nonspecific-content words that facilitate deeper understanding and communication skills. Words such as *release, convert, beneficial, produce, receive, source,* and *reflect* are words used in the investigations and *FOSS Science Resources* and are frequently used in other content areas. Learning these academic vocabulary words gives students a more precise and complex way of practicing and communicating productive thinking. Consider using the strategies described in the Science-Vocabulary Development section to explicitly teach targeted, high-leverage words that can be used in multiple ways and that can help students make connections to other words and concepts. Sentence frames, word wall, concept maps, and cognitive content dictionary are strategies that have been found to be effective with academic-vocabulary development.

▶ **NOTE**
For additional resources and updated references, go to FOSSweb.

# REFERENCES

Applebee, A. 1984. "Writing and Reasoning." *Review of Educational Research* 54 (winter): 577–596.

Bereiter, C. 2002. *Education and Mind in the Knowledge Age.* Hillsdale, NJ: Erlbaum.

Black Hills Special Services Cooperative. 2006. "3-2-1 Strategy." In *On Target: More Strategies to Guide Learning.* Rapid City, SD. http://www.sdesa6.org/content/resources.htm.

Dyasi, H. M. 2006. "Visions of Inquiry: Science." In *Linking Science and Literacy in the K–8 Classroom*, ed. R. Douglas, K. Worth, and W. Binder. Arlington, VA: NSTA Press.

Gibbons, P. 2002. *Scaffolding Language, Scaffolding Learning.* Portsmouth, NH: Heinemann.

Graham, S., and M. Herbert. 2010. *Writing to Read: Evidence for How Writing Can Improve Reading.* New York: Carnegie.

Hamilton, G. 2002. *Content-Area Reading Strategies: Science.* Portland, ME: Walch Publishing.

Hand, B., and V. Prain. 2002. "Teachers Implementing Writing-to-Learn Strategies in Junior Secondary Science: A Case Study." *Science Education* 86: 737–755.

Harvey, S. 1998. *Nonfiction Matters: Reading, Writing, and Research in Grades 3–8.* Portland, ME: Stenhouse.

Harvey, S., and A. Goudvis. 2007. *Strategies That Work: Teaching Comprehension for Understanding and Engagement.* Portland, ME: Stenhouse.

Keene, E., and S. Zimmermann. 2007. *Mosaic of Thought: The Power of Comprehension Strategies.* 2nd ed. Portsmouth, NH: Heinemann.

Keys, C. 1999. *Revitalizing Instruction in Scientific Genres: Connecting Knowledge Production with Writing to Learn in Science.* Athens: University of Georgia.

Lieberman, G. A., and L. L. Hoody. 1998. *Closing the Achievement Gap: Using the Environment as an Integrating Context for Learning.* San Diego, CA: State Education and Environment Roundtable.

National Research Council. 2012. *A Framework for K–12 Science Education: Practices, Crosscutting Concepts, and Core Ideas.* Committee on Conceptual Framework for New Science Education Standards.

Ostlund, K. 1998. "What the Research Says about Science Process Skills: How Can Teaching Science Process Skills Improve Student Performance in Reading, Language Arts, and Mathematics?" *Electronic Journal of Science Education* 2 (4).

Wellington, J., and J. Osborne. 2001. *Language and Literacy in Science Education*. Buckingham, UK: Open University Press.

Winokur, J., and K. Worth. 2006. "Talk in the Science Classroom: Looking at What Students and Teachers Need to Know and Be Able to Do." In *Linking Science and Literacy in the K–8 Classroom*, ed. R. Douglas, K. Worth, and W. Binder. Arlington, VA: NSTA Press.

# Taking FOSS Outdoors

# Taking FOSS Outdoors

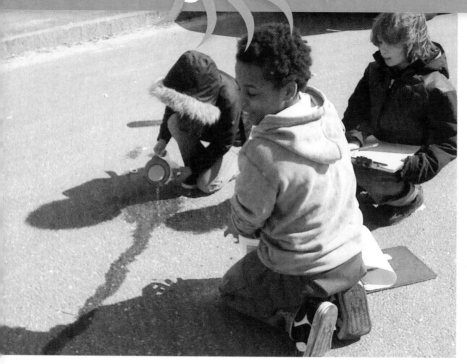

*If we want children to flourish, to become truly empowered, then let us allow them to love the earth before we ask them to save it.*

**David Sobel,** *Beyond Ecophobia*

## INTRODUCTION

During its first 20 years, FOSS focused on classroom science. The goal was to develop a scientifically literate population with an ever-growing knowledge of the natural world and the interactions and organizational models that govern and explain it. In recent years, it has become clear that we have a larger responsibility to the students we touch with our program. We have to extend classroom learning into the field to bring the science concepts and principles to life. In the process of validating classroom learning among the schoolyard trees and shrubs, down in the weeds on the asphalt, and in the sky overhead, students will develop a relationship with nature. It is our relationship with natural systems that allows us to care deeply for these systems. In order for students in our schools today to save Earth, and save it they must, they first have to feel the pulse, smell the breath, and hear the music of nature. So pack up your explorer's kit, throw open the door, and join us. We're taking FOSS outdoors.

### Contents

# WHAT DOES FOSS LOOK LIKE OUTDOORS?

Visualize taking FOSS outdoors: Students exit the classroom in an orderly fashion, their direction and purpose undeterred by the joyful sounds of other students at recess. With focused enthusiasm, the band of young scientists moves toward the edge of the schoolyard. Each student is carrying something, maybe a clipboard for recording, a container for collecting, or a hand lens for observing. Students reach their destination and quickly form a sharing circle. After a brief orientation, students disperse and begin searching the tall grass along the chain-link fence. All are independently recording in their science notebooks, and all are on task. The teacher moves about with intention, speaking to a few students at a time. After several more minutes of this work, the teacher rings a chime. Students freeze, raise one arm, and look at her. She rings the chime again. Students leave their materials in their spots and re-form their sharing circle with their teacher for discussion or additional instructions.

This scenario could be anywhere in the country with a regular classroom teacher using any of the FOSS modules. Taking FOSS outdoors is a natural extension of the classroom work. It looks and feels a lot like standard FOSS activities. Many of the routines you use inside the classroom can be implemented outdoors as well. Success, however, does depend on a few specialized skills and specific preparation to maximize outdoor teaching efficiency.

Expect the enthusiasm, participation, engagement, group discussions, and effort on notebook entries to be heightened during and after an outdoor experience. Even the simplest outdoor activities create a surge of positive energy. It is difficult to determine whether the enthusiasm and commitment students exhibit when doing FOSS outdoors comes from exercising content they already know or from just being outdoors. Students can be a bit louder and more excited when they are learning outdoors, and the space allows for this expansion in energy level, which benefits some students immensely.

# GOALS AND OBJECTIVES

The three program goals set down 20 years ago still serve FOSS well. They are: (1) scientific literacy for all students, (2) instructional efficiency and support for teachers, and (3) systemic reform.

The march into the schoolyard has three objectives that relate to the goal for students. First, the outdoor activities **continue and extend the learning** that starts in the classroom. The outdoor activities provide more experience with the content and additional opportunities to practice skills and techniques developed in the classroom.

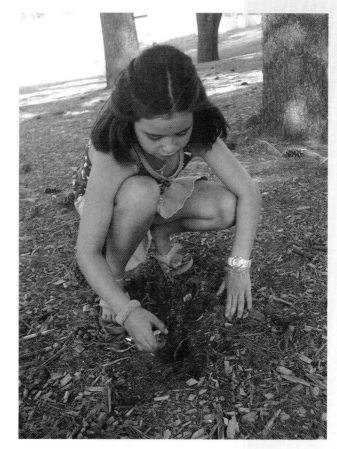

Second, venturing out provides opportunities for students to discover **applications and examples of classroom content and concepts**. The classroom activities work well for developing sound conceptual science knowledge. That knowledge, however, is constrained by the context in which the concepts are taught. For students to take the next level of ownership of that knowledge, they need to see how it applies and generalizes in the broader context of the world. Leaving the classroom context with a head full of new ideas and new tools for observation enriches the learning.

The third objective is to **connect students with nature**. On the boundaries of the planned, structured experiences are the intangibles that may spark a new relationship with natural systems. It may start with a multisensory experience in the native environment—wind, cold, sunshine, plants, insects, on and on—and advance to an awareness of the diversity of resources surrounding the school. It might evolve into a consciousness of place, followed by a flood of questions about the structure, organization, and operation of the schoolyard ecosystem. When students bond with nature, they have accepted a precious gift, and we have accomplished something important.

# MANAGING SPACE

FOSS outdoor activities are designed to be successful in a diversity of schoolyards. Some schoolyards are covered in asphalt, while others have been turned into well-designed outdoor learning environments. Some include large, grassy areas without trees, and others are covered with mulch. One outdoor space may be circled by a variety of mature trees; the next may have recently planted maples and pines scattered about. The space may reflect thoughtful attention or neglect. Nevertheless, FOSS believes that bringing students into the fresh air under a changing sky, into the available outdoor space, will awaken their well-being and stimulate their understanding of science concepts.

## Choosing Outdoor Spaces

Whether your school's landscape is wild, manicured, or asphalt, there are more options for outdoor learning spaces than might initially meet the eye. This section will help you choose the best spaces near your school for the FOSS outdoor activity.

Before choosing your outdoor study areas, get to know your outdoor spaces. Look closely at all areas surrounding the school building—even places that students do not normally go. Many seemingly uninteresting

monoculture fields are flourishing with a diversity of different grass species and other small flowering plants. Consider the pile of leaves that blew into a corner of your schoolyard; a crack in the concrete; or the ragged, weedy edge of the field where the lawn mower doesn't reach. These are places that provide small animals with what they need—food, shelter, water, and space. Transition zones where vegetation changes from shrubbery to lawn or garden to field can present interesting study sites. As you ponder the learning possibilities in and around your schoolyard, consider these characteristics.

***Accessibility.*** You should be able to walk from your classroom to your outdoor site in 2–5 minutes. Sites farther than 10 minutes away can be considered for special outings, but are not realistic for frequent access. Check out physical access if you have students whose mobility requires consideration. Be aware of slippery surfaces from water or ice, and caution students to be careful.

**Purpose.** Determine the space needs of the activity. Some activities will require open space, such as a field or blacktop. Other activities work better if students have a more diverse landscape with varying environmental conditions (such as temperature, light intensity, wind). Some activities require a variety of human-made materials to measure or test for certain properties (such as magnets to test for magnetism). Different areas will serve different needs.

**Size.** The space should be large enough for the class to work comfortably but small enough for you to supervise all students easily. You always need to be able to see all your students, and your students need to be close enough to hear you and your attention signal.

**Boundaries.** For any space you intend to use, make sure you have clearly defined the boundaries before heading outdoors with your students. Ideally, the landscape will be helpful. For example, stay between the sidewalk and the tree line. If natural markers are not present, you may need to bring along traffic cones or their equivalent to define limits. In general, consider if there are any hazards, such as dangerous debris, poisonous plants, or traffic.

## Fostering and Maintaining Diversity

For life science and earth science studies, ideally you want your site to have a variety of living and dead plant matter and a range of environmental conditions. Survey your site to see if it includes places that have been left unmanaged. Even a small wild zone along a fence or behind the maintenance area or an adjacent field can be a valuable resource. It is important for students to see that living things carry on, even in the city, without human assistance.

**Enhancing your schoolyard.** You may be able to secure a small section of the schoolyard from the school custodian, allowing it to grow wild to compare to the managed school grounds. Consult with your custodian and principal to see if this can be arranged.

Another way to enhance biodiversity is to encourage decomposition by letting fallen leaves and/or lawn clippings to remain on an area of soil over the winter. This gives worms and other decomposers something to eat, which, in turn, provides food for everything else. Make sure all necessary parties are aware of your intentions to leave an area untouched. If you find that you need administrative permission, consider ways to contain and mark the unkempt (but not unloved) area so that it clearly represents an intentional project.

***Tread lightly.*** Your schoolyard study areas will potentially experience some user impact. It is important to teach students to minimize their environmental footprint. Otherwise, the living things they disturb might seek a safer place to live. Unless the class is intentionally collecting specimens, nothing natural should be picked up or removed from the area. This is a good opportunity to introduce the "leave no trace" philosophy, which, in an effort to preserve an area for recreation, encourages us to leave natural objects as we find them.

At some schools, the outdoor space is used by so many classrooms that a system is needed to schedule outdoor activities. A sign-up sheet can be used to reserve outdoor spaces just as is done to reserve other school resources. Check the site the morning before taking the class outdoors to make sure the area is ready for students to investigate.

## Weather

Weather can present great challenges and exceptional experiences. Inclement weather can provide an excellent opportunity to study environmental concepts: water drainage, wind impact, plant and animal survival adaptations. (There is nothing like being out in a snowstorm to appreciate the value of insulation!) Making extra preparations to study out in the elements has value. If the activity can be undertaken with some assurance of success, try to make it work. Over time, students acclimate to all sorts of weather and will actually look forward to the challenge of going out in difficult weather.

***Clothing.*** The right gear at the right time can make all the difference. Baseball caps stored at school can work well in a light rain and are often essential as sun protection in warmer climates. Baseball caps in a light rain are especially helpful for students who wear glasses. If possible, invest in a set of rain ponchos to make it possible to go out in wet weather. Large trash bags can make very effective, low-cost ponchos. Of course, you will want to model this elegant attire. Communicate regularly with students and family members about upcoming outdoor experiences.

***Wind.*** A stiff breeze can fling your materials into disarray or send notebooks flying. If you anticipate wind, discuss ways to keep materials from blowing away (such as using natural paperweights or taping down nonliving specimens). If there is a protected area where you and your class can take shelter briefly, the activity can continue. You may have to chase down a couple of notebook sheets before students become accustomed to securing papers and other light materials.

## Safety and Comfort

Be prepared for the unexpected. Insect stings (ants, bees, wasps, mosquitoes) can be alarmingly painful for young students, particularly if they have not been stung before. Although extremely unlikely in a schoolyard, have a plan developed with students in advance as to how to retreat with purpose if someone accidentally disturbs a nest. You should already know who is allergic and who has never been stung before.

Skin-irritating plants (poison oak, poison ivy, poison sumac, nettles) can certainly put a damper on a field trip. Take a moment, and get to know your local irritants and toxic plants. The rule "leaves of three, let it be" works only for poison ivy and poison oak. Poison sumac has 7–13 leaves on a branch. Stinging nettle feels much like being stung by a jellyfish and can be very frightening for students who have never experienced it. Often, the irritation subsides within a few minutes; do not treat rashes with bleach or rubbing alcohol.

Lyme disease is a treatable bacterial infection, carried by deer ticks. It is present throughout the country, but is particularly present in eastern states. It is possible to get sick without finding a tick bite. If you or your students experience flulike symptoms that are severe enough to see a doctor, make sure that doctor is aware of any outdoor exposure.

If you are out and about in tick country, tuck pant legs into socks and take a few minutes at the end of the trip to pair up and look for obvious ticks on clothing and on the neck and shoulders of a partner.

# MANAGING TIME
## When to Teach

When you start a new module, anticipate when you might want to go outdoors, and schedule the time. The At a Glance chart in each investigation can help with this planning.

***Time of year.*** If possible, plan the time of year when you will teach particular modules. In the northern tier, life science and earth science modules would be best in the fall or spring. In the southern tier, it might be best to teach life science modules in the winter when it is not uncomfortably hot during the day. Good times to coordinate your outdoor activities with the school calendar include minimum days or other disruptions to the regular schedule, days just before or after school vacations, and days following district testing.

***Time of day.*** Consider the time of day you teach your activities. Established schedules are often difficult to alter, but you might find it advantageous to do so. If you do a lot of seat work in the mornings, you may want to break the routine occasionally with an outdoor activity. Students will return to the classroom refreshed and ready to focus on the next seated activity you have planned.

If you live in a climate where it gets really hot during the school day, you might want to teach outdoors early in the day. Conversely, if you live in a cold climate, you might want to do your winter outdoor activities midday. If you're looking for wildlife (birds, insects, mammals), the best time to go outdoors might be in the morning.

If you plan to use a part of the schoolyard that is heavily populated at predictable times during the day (lunch, physical education), plan to venture out at a time when other activities are minimal.

Stay flexible. If you are studying the **Water Module**, for example, be prepared to dash out if it rains or snows. One of the delights of outdoor education is going out when nature is putting on a show. Inquiring minds rush out for the experience when timid observers retreat.

***Specific times.*** Some activities require a sunny day. Measuring shadows, solar water heaters, and solar cell investigations require sunshine. It can be tricky to move on without completing specific observations or experiments. Be creative. You may need to proceed with the module and return to the sunny-day activity when the Sun finally comes out.

## Instructional Time

An outdoor activity might require 15 minutes, or it might require an hour. Only part of the time budgeted for outdoor learning is actually spent interacting with the schoolyard terrain, plants, and animals. The rest is management.

***Travel time.*** It will take perhaps 10 minutes from the announcement that it is time to decamp for the schoolyard and the time you arrive there. It will take several minutes to describe and distribute materials, get the appropriate clothing, line up, and travel in an orderly fashion to the designated location. Travel back to the classroom will take another 3–4 minutes.

***Instructions.*** Outdoors, students form a sharing circle. It will take 2–4 minutes to review rules, set the boundaries for the activity, describe the challenge, and distribute materials.

***Investigation time.*** Students break into pairs or groups to engage in the outdoor investigation. This might be as short as 8–10 minutes or as long as 30–40 minutes.

***Wrap-up.*** Students return to the sharing circle to share and discuss their discoveries for several minutes.

***Classroom follow-up.*** Frequently, students bring artifacts back to class to display in a classroom museum or to set up for further observation.

▶ **SAFETY NOTE**
Students should not disturb or collect live organisms in their natural habitats.

Some outdoor activities call for more flexible allocations of time. An activity may call for setup early in the day with periodic monitoring or measuring throughout the day.

# MANAGING MATERIALS

When students step onto the schoolyard, they are field scientists. In the field, there is no lab bench where investigations can be set up, and there is no ready supply of materials. The field equipment must be minimal, portable, and durable so that it can be easily and safely transported from the classroom and back.

## Field Equipment

A student's outdoor bag will contain the specific materials needed for the activity of the day as well as some core necessities, such as a hand lens and a writing tool.

Student outdoor bags might contain these basics.

- Pencils/pens
- Hand lens on brightly colored string or yarn
- Colored pencils or crayons
- Measuring tape
- Vials with caps
- Clipboard or notebook
- Seat pad

Note that pens and pencils each have drawbacks: pencil points break, and pen ink freezes in extremely cold weather. Seat pads can simply be several sheets of newspaper covered with a plastic bag.

Your basic teacher's outdoor equipment bag will include a few backup student materials and some items for helping with management.

- Extra pencils, pens, hand lenses, vials, and cups
- Attention signal (chime, whistle, or cowbell)
- Tissues and paper towels
- Basic first-aid kit (adhesive bandages)
- Phone (if leaving the school grounds)
- Student class list (particularly if you teach more than one class) with appropriate student health information and/or permission slips if away from school.

## Transporting Materials

Getting materials to and from the outdoor site is a shared responsibility. Students will carry their personal equipment, and class materials can be distributed among students or tackled as a teacher task. Students always carry something to the outdoor site, even when it would be easier for you to carry everything. This reminds students that they are heading out for science, not recess. A hand lens serves as such a token.

Some teachers prefer to have students carry only their clipboards or notebooks and pencils, while the teachers carry all the field equipment in a canvas shopping bag or milk crate to the outdoor home base. Other teachers use a wagon or wheelie crate to transport the equipment. After teaching a few outdoor activities, you will discover what works best for you. Students will get excited when they see you preparing your transport system for an outdoor activity.

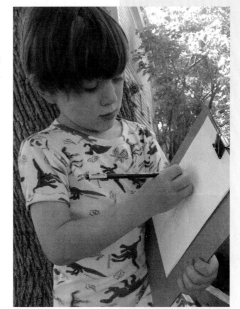

**Water.** Water is often used during outdoor activities. If you are lucky, there will be a tap near your study site. More likely, you will carry water from the school building. Recycled plastic jugs with screw caps and smaller bottles with screw caps are good vessels.

At times, you will want open containers of water, such as buckets or basins (for washing rocks, cleaning containers, and so on). Half-filled buckets can be carried a short distance, but basins should be carried empty and filled from jugs.

You rarely have to bring water back inside. Recycle leftover water by watering schoolyard plants. Make this practice overt to help students develop respect for this vital natural resource.

## Creating Outdoor Tools

A sturdy writing surface is essential for science in the schoolyard. A bound notebook (composition book) is excellent. A serviceable clipboard can be made from a piece of cardboard and a binder clip. Use a paper cutter to cut sturdy cardboard slightly larger than a sheet of notebook paper. Place a medium-size binder clip at the top and a large elastic band around the bottom (to keep the paper from flapping up). Tie a pencil on a brightly colored string to the binder clip.

A group writing surface is important sometimes. You can use blue painter's tape to attach a sheet of chart paper temporarily to a wall or clip it onto a chain-link fence with binder clips or clothespins. On windy days, attach all four corners.

A small pack can serve as a hands-free means for students to tote their equipment. Little backpacks are excellent, but a serviceable low-cost satchel can be crafted from a large plastic bag and string. Purchase enough gallon-size zip bags for your class. Punch two holes just *under* the ends of the zipper. (This reduces tearing.) Cut the strings about 1 meter long. Tie sturdy knots that will not come undone. Store the string inside the bag after use to prevent tangling with other bags.

Hand lenses may disappear when students place them on the ground to perform a task. Run bright-colored string or yarn through holes in the lenses for students to wear. If your hand lenses do not already have holes, see if you can get holes drilled through the handles.

# MANAGING STUDENTS

Going outdoors regularly is the best way to develop a productive and joyful working relationship with students in the outdoors. When students realize that going outdoors to learn is not a special event but, rather, a science event that will occur routinely, you may be surprised at how quickly they adapt to their expanded, enriched classroom.

## Before the First Outing

It is always important to let the school administration know that you and your students will periodically be out of the classroom. If you are planning to leave the school grounds, remember to file a flight plan describing your itinerary, anticipated time of return, and contact partners.

At the beginning of the school year, send a letter home to families, letting them know that learning will extend to the schoolyard and, possibly, beyond. It may be possible to have a signed permission slip for impromptu walking field trips outside the schoolyard. Have families put their contact information and specific student health information on the permission slip. Photocopy these, and have one set of copies in the office and another set in a zip bag in your outdoor equipment bag for emergencies.

Tell students at the beginning of the year that they will be going outdoors often during science class. Remember to let them know a day in advance that they will be going outdoors. Let them know what it means to dress appropriately. This is especially important in the cold or stormy season when students will need proper clothing for safety and comfort. Your class can go out in any weather if students are dressed appropriately. A consistent system of reminders and clothing preparation will train students to be prepared.

***Safety rules.*** Creating consistent, considerate rules of engagement is important. Learning is enhanced, and behavior problems are largely averted by routines that students participate in and understand.

Have a discussion about what students think constitutes proper preparation and behavior for leaving the classroom to study outdoors. (This discussion may be most productive *after* an initial orientation

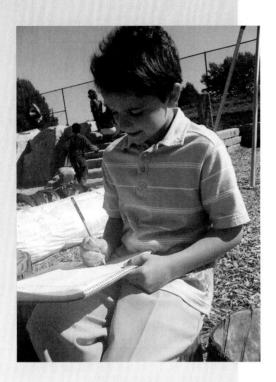

excursion to survey the schoolyard resources.) Have students generate a list of behaviors that they can adopt and respect. You may want to generate a second list of behaviors that you will agree to as leader of the adventure. Introduce as much formality into the process as you deem important. Develop the idea of a contract that all members of the class sign. Post the contract in your classroom and reference the *Outdoor Safety* poster. Here are the behaviors and rules that should appear on the list.

- Walk quickly and quietly outdoors.

- Outdoor science is not recess.

- Listen to the teacher's instructions.

- Freeze when the teacher rings the bell.

- Stay inside the boundaries.

- Don't make noise near the classrooms.

- Don't injure plants and animals in any way.

- Leave the outdoor environment the way you found it. Never release living organisms into the local environment unless they were collected there.

## First Outing

Your first trip to the schoolyard may be a bit chaotic. Students may be distracted by other activities going on, and they may lapse into recess mode. A few precautions will minimize disruptive behaviors.

***The path of egress.*** Determine which doors are available to access your outdoor site. Make sure you follow your school's policy for using auxiliary doors during the school day. Do they need to be closed at all times, or can you prop one open? Are they locked from the outside? You may be able to access keys in order to reduce travel time. When possible, avoid using the door you would normally use for recess. Students have a different mind-set when they walk onto the schoolyard through the "outdoor classroom" door.

***Orientation activity.*** Consider an orientation activity for your first outing. The stated goal might be a site tour to inventory the resources on hand. Your primary agenda, however, is to dissipate the energy generated by the novelty of leaving the classroom during class time. Focus on preparing your transition to the outdoors, moving out in a purposeful and orderly fashion and arriving at your predetermined "home base," a destination that you will always go to initially when you leave the classroom. Form a sharing circle, a process you will use time and again. Tour the schoolyard, proceeding as a whole group, then ask students to walk as individuals for a few minutes, then with a partner for a minute, and finally with a group of four. This gives students a brief experience with each of the four ways they will be organized for various outdoor activities. End with another sharing circle and an orderly return to the classroom.

**Challenging students.** Sometimes the class will be inattentive and unresponsive. At such times, it is appropriate to direct students back to the classroom. Breaking the contract has consequences, and students need to understand that the opportunity to learn in nature is a privilege. They will remember that day.

In rare instances, you may have an individual student who is regularly not able to comply. Interestingly, this is probably not the student who you anticipated would have difficulty. Often, students who have difficulty with attention and performance in traditional classroom seat work shine and take leadership outdoors. In the case of the noncompliant student, it may be necessary to ask him or her to take a time-out if he or she is able to sit without disrupting others' experiences. If the bad behavior persists, you may be obliged to return to the classroom early. Even so, it is important to give the student a chance to redeem himself or herself the next time you go outdoors.

## Routines

Routines are good for management. They impose a measure of self-monitoring because they represent behaviors that are already known and have been practiced. If one person transgresses during a routine, other students are able to intervene to help you with student management. Here are a few routines that may work for you.

**Science door.** Have you ever watched a group of students pass through the exterior door on their way to recess? As soon as one foot hits the asphalt, they start running and cheering. It is a beautiful sight. Clearly, this is not how you want students to leave the building as you head out for science. One subtle but effective way to distinguish science from recess is to use a different door for science than for recess. Refer to this exit as the "learning door."

**Transition behavior.** Be explicit about how you want students to walk through the hallways and into the schoolyard. If students exit wildly, simply ring the bell, have them line up inside, and try it again. If this continues to be a problem, return to the classroom and try another day. By consistently showing students that this behavior limits their time outdoors, they will follow your directions.

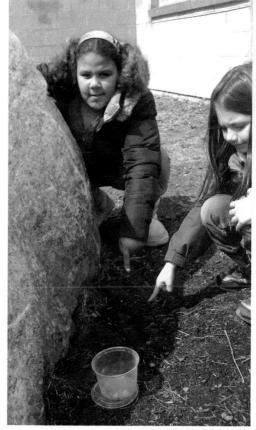

# Taking FOSS Outdoors

**Home base.** Establish a destination in the schoolyard where every outdoor activity will begin. Students should walk directly there after leaving the school building. Choose a place that is level and, if possible, away from classroom windows and popular recess areas.

**Sharing circle.** When students arrive at home base, they should form a large sharing circle—everyone in a single ring with no students hanging back. This is an effective way to maintain eye contact with all students while you give instructions or share findings. Take a position in the circle where you are facing the Sun. This way, you will know that students won't be distracted by having the Sun's glare in their eyes. A sharing circle is also used to transition from one task to another, to summarize an activity, or anytime you need to regroup.

Techniques for forming a circle vary. One method is "magnetic feet." Students spread their legs to meet their neighbors' feet. Magically, these magnets turn off when you direct them to do so. Students may also stand with hands on hips, elbows touching with neighbors'. Pick or create a method that works with your students.

To speed up the formation of a sharing circle, try the tried-and-true countdown from five, with the objective that everyone is in a proper circle by zero.

**Attention signal.** Adopt a uniform signal for attention. It is essential that students respond to the attention signal immediately. You may choose the same method you use in the classroom or, if this is not appropriate for the outdoors, try one of these.

- A chime, bell, whistle, or other singular and loud sound. These are appropriate outdoors. When students hear it, they stop, look, and listen.

- Count down from five and when you get to one, students are silent with their hands up. This might not be appropriate outdoors. A countdown from ten can be used to call students back to a sharing circle.

- Clap call and response. You clap a pattern, and students return it by repeating the clapping pattern. This works if students are all nearby.

**Focus question.** Inquiry-based activities are guided by a question. This pedagogical routine should extend into the schoolyard, too. *Students need to know why they are engaged in the outdoor investigation.* They should expect to write the focus question in their notebooks at the outset of the investigation and produce an answer at the end of the investigation.

**Boundaries.** Setting boundaries allows students freedom within a defined space. Because different activities may require different locations, it is always important to be explicit about where students are allowed to travel during the outdoor activity.

**Buddy system.** You may want to institute a buddy system, particularly if you leave the schoolyard. When participants are paired off, tell them that each individual is responsible at all times for the whereabouts and safety of his or her buddy. It is helpful and fun to number the pairs in order to count off quickly and account for everyone.

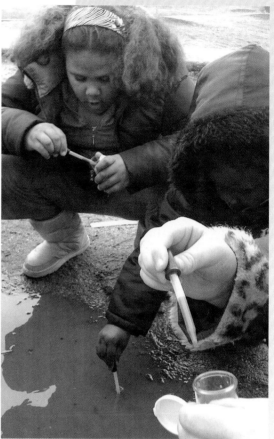

## Considerations for Students with Disabilities

FOSS evolved from pioneering work done in the 1970s with students with physical disabilities. The legacy of that work is that FOSS investigations incorporate multisensory methods, not only to accommodate students with physical and learning disabilities, but also to maximize information gathering for all students. Strategies that provide opportunities to learn for students with disabilities turn out to be good strategies for all students.

All students benefit from opportunities to experience the natural world outdoors. For students with disabilities, consider how to make the schoolyard accessible and safe so that they can work with a degree of independence. This requires advance planning to make sure that the student, his or her family, the special education teacher, and others involved in the child's school experience are informed and have input into the process.

Whenever a student with a disability is successful in a full-inclusion classroom, there is a behind-the-scenes collaborative effort of caring educators who work together to support the student with just the right amount of scaffolding. In advance of teaching the first outdoor activity, contact the special education teachers in charge of each student's Individualized Education Plan (IEP), and have them review the planned outdoor experiences. Ask the teachers to recommend modifications that will better accommodate and support each student. Invite the special educators to join the class for the outdoor activity.

**Attention and language-based disabilities.** Students with attention and behavioral issues often thrive when they are engaged in science outdoors. A fenced area will help you to both keep track of students and provide a sense of safety. Having students work with partners (buddies) allows students to look after each other. Provide short, structured opportunities for students to participate in outdoor activities in a clearly defined space, and expand the boundaries and time expectations as students earn your trust and confidence. Many educators have found great success with treating the outdoor activity as a reward for excellent behavior indoors.

Consider students' communication requirements, and plan to bring specialty devices outdoors with you. This might be as simple as some picture cue cards to help enhance your message or an electronic communication device such as a computer.

**Physical disabilities and visual impairments.** In the Getting Ready section of each outdoor activity, we ask that the teacher decide where the outdoor activity should be taught. You may find that certain locations are better than others for the purposes of developing science concepts and meeting the physical needs of students with disabilities. Get to know your schoolyard really well, and try to experience it as your students do.

One side of most schoolyards is typically a parking lot, and the other three sides have spaces accessible to students for work and play. If you have a student with a physical disability, you need to consider if the terrain provides for good mobility for the student. Often, schoolyards are handicapped accessible because they are covered in asphalt. For many of the FOSS outdoor activities, an asphalt area is appropriate to use. When you want to use a greener location, make sure wheelchairs or crutches will work on these new surfaces. If the surface will be a mobility challenge, see if a paraprofessional or an educational assistant is able to help the student. If someone is not able to join you, consider if a classmate can help. If this is not an option, then consider working at a transition zone where the grass meets the asphalt.

A student with a visual impairment should make a scouting trip to the outdoor site with a mobility instructor to get the lay of the land and to learn where things are located. If the student becomes familiar with and knows how to navigate his or her outdoor surroundings, it will allow for more independence. Even so, during the actual outdoor activity, the student may need someone to quietly describe the terrain ahead and may need a fellow student's arm for balance and security.

If a student struggles with gross motor coordination, uneven ground may present a challenge. Just as you would in the classroom, begin by offering more support, and slowly pull back on this assistance as students become more comfortable with their stamina, security, and endurance with regular outdoor activities.

**Sensory sensitivity.** For a student with tactile-sensitivity issues, make it clear that he or she may, for example, observe as a classmate digs in the soil to collect a sample. Over time, this student may feel better able to participate by using gloves or by washing his or her hands as soon as the digging is complete. Knowing where each student falls on the continuum of a disability will help you decide when to hold back asking a student to fully participate, when to allow him or her to just observe, and when to give a gentle nudge and expect more active participation.

For students with sensory disorders, the outdoors is often a calming space. Consider where the quietest place in the schoolyard is, and use this more often if you have students with sensitivity to noise.

No matter what the disability, educators have found success taking students outdoors. With advance planning, communication with the student and the special education team, and a little extra effort, you, too, can provide a rich, safe outdoor learning experience for all your students.

## TEACHING STRATEGIES

In the beginning, you may find that students regularly use descriptive terms such as "icky," "yucky," and "gross." You may have students who say things such as "I cannot get my clothes dirty. My mom will be mad." Many students are fearful of bugs, wooded areas, and even just sitting on the grass. Often, after a few outdoor activities, these fears and excuses fade away. With patience, persistence, and support, students' resistance may be overcome entirely. If you suspect that your students may be reluctant to work outdoors, structure your first few activities to be low-stress activities. The first few times outdoors can be fairly benign activities with students choosing a comfortable place to just sit (or stand), practicing writing outdoors, and doing simple collecting or counting tasks.

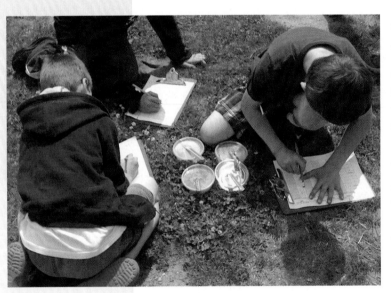

**Set the tone.** Many teaching strategies that are effective in the classroom work outdoors, too. For example, at the sharing circle, instead of instinctively talking louder (because it is noisy outdoors), kneel down and speak in a loud whisper so that students need to focus to hear you. If students are speaking, put up your silent signal, and wait for silence. The educator's voice sets the tone for the activity.

**Take a position.** In the sharing circle, position yourself where you have the Sun in your face so that students don't need to squint. If possible, place yourself next to those students who might benefit from a silent look or hand on the shoulder to remind them to be silent.

**Meet the challenge.** Students who struggle with behavior problems often respond well outdoors when given responsibility. Let the active student carry the heavy jug of water or take the position at the front of the line to lead the class outdoors. For many students, this is all it takes to get them off on the right foot for the outdoor activity.

Students who have the greatest difficulty controlling their behavior indoors are often the leaders when it comes to working in an outdoor space. You may find that students who are not as attentive or cannot sit still inside are the most insistent about quieting down so that the class can get outdoors for science.

**Get them writing.** Primary students (grades K–2) can fill out a chart on a clipboard outdoors. They are also capable of recording observations outdoors in their notebooks if observation is their only task. Most primary students will need to sit down with their clipboards on their laps or on the ground to do this successfully. In the early years, most writing follows an outdoor activity and is done inside on desks and with the classroom's word wall.

Upper-elementary students (grades 3–6) are capable of writing outdoors. Students will benefit from a quick activity about how to place the notebook or clipboard in the crook of their nonwriting arm for support.

Depending on the activity, you might decide to have students attach their notebooks to a clipboard and place the clipboards in a crate for easy transport and storage. This technique is useful when the ground is moist, when the activity is messy, or when students need to use their hands to complete the activity. The recording will happen immediately after the hands-on activity. Be open to the surprise of how much your students are capable of noticing and recording during and after an outdoor activity.

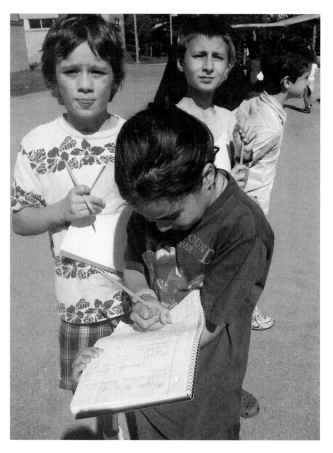

# FLOW OF OUTDOOR ACTIVITIES

The natural flow of a FOSS outdoor activity is slightly different from that of a standard FOSS indoor activity. The steps of a typical outdoor activity are listed below. This list may be helpful if you want to teach more than the handful of outdoor activities in the *Investigations Guide*, or if you want to adapt an indoor activity for schoolyard use.

1. **Prepare for the outdoor activity.**

   • Determine the best location to teach the activity.

   • Check the weather forecast.

   • Make sure students will be dressed appropriately.

   • Prepare materials for distribution.

   • Check the site the morning of the activity.

2. **Set the learning objective.**

   • Present the focus question.

   • Discuss procedures.

3. **Go outdoors.**

   • Gather at the predetermined location.

4. **Model or describe the activity.**

   • Organize students.

   • Define boundaries.

   • Introduce/distribute materials.

5. **Monitor the activity.**

   • Check student engagement.

   • Check student recording.

   • Ask questions.

6. **Share the experience.**

   • Form a sharing circle to discuss experiences.

   • Share thinking.

   • Share answers to the focus question.

7. **Return to class**

   • Make connections to the related indoor activity.

   • Display student work and collections.

# EXTENDING BEYOND FOSS OUTDOOR ACTIVITIES

Occasionally, you may stumble upon a serendipitous opportunity. A breeze may launch thousands of twirling seeds from a maple tree, a woodpecker may alight on a tree so close that students can observe it drumming for insects, student-made parachutes may be carried by an updraft high into the sky and out of sight. To your delight, you may spy something you have never seen before. It can happen at any time when you are outdoors!

At special moments like these, our job as educators is to signal students to stop and quietly appreciate the suspension of time. Sometimes, words break the wonder. Trust your instincts at magical moments like these. The answers to questions will come eventually. It is not essential to label the event or even understand it. By inviting students to be alive with their feelings in the moment, you give them a gift for a lifetime.

It is not uncommon for educators to experience the powerful effect of the outdoors on student learning. If you find yourself searching for other outdoor learning opportunities, consider the ones below.

***Move activities outdoors.*** Whatever the subject, students will have more room outdoors to be creative with some activities, and you can worry less about water, sand, and gravel spills. You must still consider how to transport materials, where students will sit, how they will return their project to the classroom, and how to clean up the outdoor space and students' hands before returning to the building.

***Use the outdoors for extensions.*** Extending an inside concept to the outdoors is an excellent way to apply new knowledge. For example, in the **Structures of Life Module**, students grow bush beans hydroponically. If the large leaves fascinate students, go outdoors and see how many kinds of leaves you can find in the schoolyard. Do they all have smooth edges and come to a point at their tips? Go on a leaf hunt, group the leaves by their characteristics, and, eventually, have students tape them into their science notebooks.

There is great value in repeating an indoor activity outdoors. If your students are sanding wood samples inside, follow this up with a trip outdoors to find a stick and sand it. Have you been studying sow bugs? Ask students if they think they know where in the schoolyard they might find these bugs. Applying what students have learned in the classroom and putting that knowledge to work outdoors is an effective way to solidify their understanding. It's also an effective way to informally assess whether students understand the concepts, as well as a method for reinforcing the learning.

▶ **NOTE**
Remember not to release
any classroom animals into
schoolyard environments.

***Find solitude.*** Use your outdoor space for silent independent work time. Just as in the classroom, the outdoor space can be a workspace with activities going on. At times, the outdoor space is more of a sanctuary for independent observation and notebook writing. It can be a place for special classroom rituals, awakening awareness of the beauty of nature. Sometimes, it can just be a place to be silent for a minute to awaken the senses and refocus students' energy. Some teachers increase this silent minute to 2, 3, or even 5 minutes. Silence is something to be practiced, and for many students and teachers, this can be challenging. This is a special way to end an outdoor experience and will help students transition into the classroom.

***Enhance biodiversity.*** Modify your schoolyard by adding natural materials, such as logs, rocks, or paving stones. These structures can provide safe havens that may attract more living things. These types of shelters can be particularly helpful if you have an environment without natural shelter from the Sun, such as trees and shrubs. Students can also be involved in the design and implementation of these projects.

Schoolyard modification of this kind requires administrative participation and the support of the school custodian. Marking the area with educational signage can further benefit the enhanced site. If your schoolyard habitat needs your intervention to cultivate biodiversity, understand that it can take a couple of years to get established. Areas completely surrounded by blacktop or concrete can become filled with living things if provided with food, shelter, and water.

***Attract wildlife.*** There are many responsible ways to attract wildlife to your class windows with feeders for birds, squirrels, hummingbirds, or butterflies, as well as many great programs for monitoring these animals. See FOSSweb for ideas for additional wildlife observation projects.

***Establish long-term studies.*** The possibilities for long-term studies are endless, ranging from weather monitoring to seasonal population variation. It can be as simple as adopting an observation location and visiting it monthly to monitor various aspects of change over time. See FOSSweb for ideas for long-term projects.

***Create gardens.*** Planting a garden in raised beds or improved soil is an ambitious option for increasing the biodiversity of your schoolyard. Consider carefully, especially with a vegetable garden, the timing of the school year. In most parts of the country, the time when plants require the most support is during summer vacation. Even if you can get a summer program involved, we suggest starting with indigenous plants that bloom or mature in spring and fall and require little maintenance.

# ELEMENTARY-LEVEL ENVIRONMENTAL EDUCATION

In the early 1990s, David Sobel noticed something poignant about children's perceptions of the environment. If a child had been introduced to environmental issues at school that were presented in the context of doom-and-gloom scenarios, the child expressed a heightened sense of anxiety and hopelessness, which Sobel calls ecophobia (Sobel 1996). The implications of his finding should raise a cautionary flag. Sobel is not suggesting that we abandon teaching about the environment in our elementary schools. He is proposing a different approach to environmental education that will bring our children into natural, healthy relationships with environmental issues.

Effective early environmental education should focus on local and ultralocal issues. What is happening in our schoolyards? What factors influence the communities of plants and animals in our neighborhoods? How do changing weather conditions affect the populations around our schools? How are our actions affecting the habitats in our schoolyards? What can we do to enhance natural systems at our schools? Elaborate rain forest projects provide little understanding and have negligible impact on students' connections to nature; researching and installing a butterfly garden or keeping an inventory of the birds in the schoolyard can be transformative. The children from Sobel's 1996 study could tell you how many species in the Amazon were going extinct each minute, but were unfamiliar with the most common plants in their schoolyard.

Time outdoors during the school day is beneficial for student learning. Students who are exposed to hands-on experiences in their local environment often become enthusiastic, self-motivated learners and, typically, academically outperform their peers who do not have these learning opportunities (Liebermann and Hoody 1998). Children are able to pay attention for longer periods of time outdoors on the same assignment and are more focused when they return to their indoor class work (Louv 2008).

Research has produced evidence that using the schoolyard is an effective way to enhance student learning. Texas A&M University, in conjunction with the Texas Education Agency, conducted a meta-analysis of the research in order to identify and rank effective instructional methods for science education and to define how best to improve student achievement. The highest-ranked teaching strategy was Enhanced Context Strategies, which included taking meaningful field trips and using the schoolyard for activities (Scott et al. 2005).

Students' attitudes toward learning are influenced by simple outdoor experiences. In one study (Shaw and Terrance 1981), students who experienced outdoor instruction reported that, in general, they enjoyed school more and felt more supported and trusted by their teacher than they had prior to the outdoor experiences. These pretest/posttest differences were more pronounced for students who had been identified as being "uninvolved" in the classroom activities. Also, this student perception was a lasting effect that carried over to the regular classroom activities weeks later.

Perhaps the most important benefit of incorporating the outdoors into the traditional school learning environment is that it offers opportunities for students to synthesize concepts and personal experience by applying what they have learned to a new environment.

FOSS outdoor activities will help you focus on age-appropriate environmental topics and enable you to create meaningful and personal connections between your students and their local environment. When students can openly explore the environment, they can create meaningful connections to their learning and establish positive relationships with nature. You'll be amazed by what students notice.

Here's the good news. If you focus on inquiry and direct experience instead of problems, it takes remarkably little guidance for students to make positive, empowering, lifelong connections to nature. One insightful young man explained, "My video games have a pattern that is always the same, but nature is like a game that is different every time you play." As an educator, you can draw out that sense of wonder and curiosity for students while simultaneously helping them build a solid science foundation.

# REFERENCES

Liebermann, G., and L. Hoody. 1998. *Closing the Achievement Gap: Using the Environment as an Integrated Context for Learning; Results of a National Study.* San Diego: State Education and Environment Roundtable.

Louv, R. 2008. *Last Child in the Woods: Saving Our Children from Nature-Deficit Disorder.* New York: Workman Publishing.

Scott, T. et al. 2005. *Texas Science Initiative Meta-Analysis of National Research Regarding Science Teaching.* Texas Education Agency.

Shaw, T. J., and J. M. Terrance. 1981. "Involved and Uninvolved Student Perceptions in Indoor and Outdoor School Settings." *Journal of Early Adolescence,* 1:135–146.

Sobel, D. 1996. *Beyond Ecophobia: Reclaiming the Heart in Nature Education.* Great Barrington, MA: Orion Society.

## ACKNOWLEDGMENTS

The Taking FOSS Outdoors initiative got its start through a collaboration with the Boston Schoolyard Initiative (BSI). In 2004, BSI began developing an approach to teaching science that routinely takes students into the schoolyard to test, apply, and explore core science concepts and skills. As part of this project, BSI developed *Science in the Schoolyard Guides*™ for 12 FOSS modules and a companion *Science in the Schoolyard*™ DVD. In partnership with the City of Boston, BSI designs and builds schoolyards that provide a rich environment for teaching, learning, and play. For more information on BSI, *Science in the Schoolyard*, or BSI's *Outdoor Writer's Workshop*™ professional development program and materials, see www.schoolyards.org.

# FOSSweb and Technology

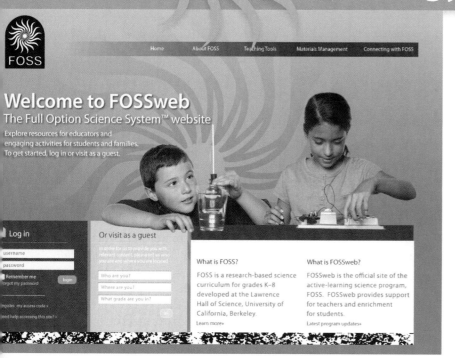

## Contents

# INTRODUCTION

FOSS is committed to providing a rich, accessible technology experience for all FOSS users. FOSSweb is the Internet access to FOSS digital resources (www.FOSSweb.com). It provides enrichment for students and support for teachers, administrators, and families who are actively involved in implementing and enjoying FOSS materials.

- Teachers can seek tips for enhancing specific modules; locate appropriate print, video, and web-based resources; discover classroom management ideas; watch teacher-preparation videos; and find information concerning plant and animal care.

- Students will enjoy the module-specific activities on FOSSweb. They can further their science investigations virtually and exercise new skills and knowledge by using the interactive simulations and media. Students can bring FOSS into their homes and share experiences with their families.

- Families can view and download information about FOSS modules, including module summaries, vocabulary, home/school connections, and other resources.

This chapter provides an overview of FOSSweb for teachers, information to help you set up your FOSSweb account, technical requirements for FOSSweb, and information on troubleshooting.

# FOSSWEB FOR ELEMENTARY CLASSROOMS

▶ **NOTE**

The FOSS digital resources are available online on FOSSweb. You can always access the most up-to-date technology information, including help and troubleshooting, on FOSSweb. The latest version of this chapter is also available as a PDF file on FOSSweb.

FOSSweb provides educators and families background on the FOSS Program, resources for materials management, general teaching tools for FOSS, purchasing links, contact information for the FOSS Project, and technical support. You do not need an account to view this general FOSS Program information. In addition to the general information, FOSSweb provides digital access to module and materials information, PDF versions of the *Teacher Resources* component of the *Teacher Toolkit*, and digital-only resources that supplement the print and kit materials for each module.

To access all the teacher resources and to set up customized pages for using FOSS, you must register and log in to FOSSweb. You can easily register and log in to your FOSSweb account from the FOSSweb homepage. Once logged in, you can customize your homepage and set up easy access to the digital components of the modules you teach. Teachers with a FOSSweb account can also create class pages with notes and assignments for each class.

▶ **NOTE**

See the Requirements for Accessing FOSSweb section for more information on creating a FOSSweb account.

A FOSSweb account is required for teachers, administrators, students, and families who wish to access customized FOSSweb content. Account login codes identify the user level so that sensitive information and data, such as assessment masters, are available only to teachers and administrators.

Here are some of the resources to support teachers using FOSS. Access to some of these resources requires an account (indicated below with an asterisk, ★). It is recommended that you access FOSSweb before beginning to teach your first FOSS module, as you will need to register for and set up a teacher user account.

## Module Information

▶ **NOTE**

Access to some of these resources requires an account. Those resources are indicated with an asterisk, ★.

- **Resources by investigation.★** The resource list links to student sheets, assessment masters, teacher masters, and multimedia for each investigation in a module.

- **Module summary.** The summary describes each investigation in a module, including major concepts developed.

- **Module updates.** Important updates cover teacher materials, student equipment, and safety considerations.

- **Module teaching notes.** These notes include teaching suggestions and enhancements to the module, sent in by experienced FOSS users.

- **Home/school connection.** These masters include an introductory letter home (with ideas to reinforce the concepts being taught) and the home/school connection sheets.

- **Teacher-preparation video.★** The video presents information to help you prepare for a module, including detailed investigation information, equipment setup and use, safety, and what students do and learn through each part of the investigation.

- **Investigations eGuide.★** The eGuide is the complete FOSS *Investigations Guide* component of the *Teacher Toolkit* in an electronic web-based format. If your district rotates modules among several teachers, this option allows all teachers easy access to the *Investigations Guide* at all times.

## Materials

- **Module kit contents.** This list, organized by drawer, shows the materials included in the FOSS kit for the module.

- **Plant and animal care.** This section includes information on caring for organisms used in the investigations.

- **Materials Safety Data Sheets (MSDS).** These sheets have information from materials manufacturers on the safe handling and disposal of materials.

- **Equipment photo cards.★** The cards provide labeled photos of equipment supplied in each FOSS kit.

## Teacher Resources

FOSSweb provides PDF files of several chapters from *Teacher Resources*. The files (Science Notebooks, Science-Centered Language Development, Taking FOSS Outdoors, FOSSweb and Technology, Notebook Masters★, Teacher Masters★, and Assessment Masters★) can be printed for classroom use.

## Digital-Only Resources

Some of the resources on FOSSweb are not found in the printed *Teacher Toolkit* and are found only on FOSSweb. Some of these resources can be used by students at home or by you as part of classroom instruction. Other resources are designed primarily for you during instruction.

- **Multimedia activities.** The multimedia simulations and activities were designed to support student learning. They include virtual investigations and student tutorials that you can use to support students who have difficulties with the materials or who have been absent.

▶ **NOTE**
Masters are available online in English and Spanish. Notebook masters are available in different formats—notebook-size half sheets and full-size sheets for projecting or printing.

- **Virtual investigations.**★ There is a set of two or three virtual investigations available for each FOSS module for grades 3–6. All the investigations require students to record data and answer concluding questions in their notebooks. In some cases, the notebook sheet used in the classroom investigation is also used for the virtual investigation.

- **Student media library.** A variety of media enhance student learning. Formats include photos, videos, an audio version of each student book, and frequently asked science questions. These resources are also available to students when they log in with a student account.

- **Recommended books and websites.** This list includes FOSS-recommended books and websites that relate to the module and are appropriate for students as well as books for teachers.

- **Vocabulary.** The word list has science-related vocabulary and definitions used in the module.

- **Focus questions.** The focus questions for each investigation are formatted for classroom projection and for printing out so that students can glue each focus question into their science notebooks. The questions can also be printed on labels.

- **Interactive whiteboard resources.**★ You can use these slide shows and other resources for grades 3–6 with an interactive whiteboard.

- **Streaming video.**★ Some video clips are part of the instruction in the investigation, and others extend concepts presented in a module.

- **FOSSmap and online assessments.**★ An online assessment system allows students to take benchmark assessments (I-Checks and Survey/Posttest) online. You can review those assessments online. Tutorial sessions based on assessment performance are also accessible for grades 3–6.

## Premium Content

In addition to the free resources available on FOSSweb, Delta Education also offers access to premium content from any Internet-enabled computer.

- **Student eBooks.**★ Student eBooks provide access to *FOSS Science Resources*. The eBooks look identical to print resources, with easy-to-turn pages, a chapter menu for easy navigation, audio clips for all text, and highlighted vocabulary words with pop-up definitions. The eBooks ensure that all students receive extra reading support.

▶ **NOTE**
The focus questions are formatted to be printed on 1" × 2⅝" mailing labels.

▶ **NOTE**
For more information about FOSS premium content, including pricing and ordering, contact your local Delta sales representative by visiting www.DeltaEducation.com or by calling 1-800-258-1302.

# REQUIREMENTS FOR ACCESSING FOSSWEB

To get started, you'll need a computer with Internet access and some additional plug-ins. Once you're online, you'll create a FOSSweb account. All information in this section is updated on FOSSweb as needed.

## Creating a FOSSweb Teacher Account

By creating a FOSSweb user account, you can personalize FOSSweb for easy access to the modules you are teaching. When you log in, you can access Resources by Investigation for each module through My FOSS Modules. This makes it simple to select the investigation and part you are teaching and view all the digital resources connected to that part.

Students and families can also access module resources from FOSSweb. You can set up class pages where students will be able to access notes from you about assignments and multimedia.

***Setting up an account.*** Set up an account on FOSSweb so that you can access the site when you begin teaching a module. FOSSweb registration information, including an access code is included with the purchase of your kit. Go to FOSSweb to register your access code—complete registration instructions are available there. If you cannot find your FOSSweb registration information and access code, contact your school administrator, your district science coordinator, or the purchasing agent for your school or district.

***Logging in to FOSSweb.*** Once your account is set up, go to FOSSweb and log in. Take the opportunity to set up your profile and customize your homepage so that your modules are included in your list in My FOSS Modules.

Familiarize yourself with the layout of the site and the additional resources available by using your account login. From your module page, you will be able to access teacher masters, assessment masters, notebook sheets, multimedia, and other digital resources described earlier in this chapter. Explore Resources by Investigation, as this will help you plan. It lists the multimedia, notebook sheets, teacher masters, and readings for each investigation part.

**Setting up class pages and student accounts.** To enable your students to log in to FOSSweb to access the multimedia and see class assignments, set up a class page and generate a user name and password for the class. To do so, log in to FOSSweb and go to your homepage. Under My Class Pages, follow the instructions to create a new class page and to leave notes for students.

## FOSSweb Technical Requirements

To use FOSSweb, your computer must meet minimum system requirements and have a compatible browser and recent versions of Flash® Player, QuickTime™, and Adobe® Reader. The system requirements are subject to change. It is strongly recommended that you visit FOSSweb to review the most recent minimum system requirements.

When using FOSSweb, you can check your browser to confirm that it has the minimum requirements to support the multimedia. You can do so by accessing the Tech Specs and Info page on FOSSweb.

**Preparing your browser.** FOSSweb requires a supported browser for Windows or Mac OS with a current version of the Flash Player plug-in, the QuickTime plug-in, and Adobe Reader or an equivalent PDF reader program. You may need administrator privileges on your computer in order to install the required programs and/or help from your school's technology coordinator.

By accessing the Tech Specs page on FOSSweb, you can check compatibility for each computer you will use to access FOSSweb, including your classroom computer, computers in a school computer lab, or a home computer. The information on FOSSweb contains the most up-to-date technical requirements.

**Support for plug-ins and reader.** Flash Player and Adobe Reader are available on www.Adobe.com as free downloads. QuickTime is available for free from www.apple.com. FOSS does not support these programs. Please go to the program's website for troubleshooting information.

## Other Multimedia Considerations

***Firewall or proxy settings.*** If your school has a firewall or proxy server, contact your IT administrator to add explicit exceptions in your proxy server and firewall for the following servers: FOSSweb.com and streamingmediahosting.com.

***Classroom technology setup.*** FOSS has a number of digital resources and makes every effort to accommodate users with different levels of access to technology. The digital resources can be used in a variety of ways and can be adapted to a number of classroom setups.

Teachers with classroom computers and an LCD projector, interactive whiteboard, or a large screen will be able to show multimedia to the class. If you have access to a computer lab, or enough computers in your classroom for students to work in small groups, you can set up time for students to use the FOSSweb digital resources during the school day. Teachers who have access to only a single computer will find a variety of beneficial resources on FOSSweb that can be used to assist with teacher preparation and materials management.

***Displaying multimedia content.*** Throughout each module, you may occasionally want to project multimedia components for instruction through your computer. To do this, you will need a computer with Internet access and either an LCD projector with a large screen, an interactive whiteboard, or a document camera arranged for the class to see.

You might want to display the notebook and teacher masters to the class. In Resources by Investigation, you'll have the option of downloading the masters to project or to copy. Choose "to project" if you plan on projecting to the class. These masters are optimized for a projection system and allow you to type onto them while they are displayed. The "to copy" versions are sized to minimize paper use when photocopying for the class.

If this projection technology is not available to you, consider making transparencies of the notebook and teacher masters for use with an overhead projector when the Getting Ready section indicates a need to project these sheets.

▶ **NOTE**
FOSSweb activities are designed for a minimum screen size of 1024 × 768. It is recommended that you adjust your screen resolution to 1024 × 768 or higher.

# TROUBLESHOOTING AND TECHNICAL SUPPORT

If you experience trouble with FOSSweb, you can troubleshoot in a variety of ways.

1. Test your browser to make sure you have the correct plug-in and browser versions. Even if you have the necessary plug-ins installed on your computer, they may not be recent enough to run FOSSweb correctly. Go to FOSSweb, and select the Tech Specs page to review the most recent system requirements and check your browser.

2. Check the FAQs on FOSSweb for additional information that may help resolve the problem.

3. Try emptying the cache from your browser and/or quitting and relaunching.

4. Restart your computer, and make sure all computer hardware turns on and is connected correctly.

If you are still experiencing problems after taking these steps, e-mail FOSS Technical Support at support@FOSSweb.com. In addition to describing the problem you are experiencing, include the following information about your computer: Mac or PC, operating system, browser and version, plug-ins and versions. This will help us troubleshoot the problem.

# Science Notebook Masters

# Plant Picture

Date _____

Observations _____

_____

_____

_____

_____

FOSS Plants and Animals Module
© The Regents of the University of California
Can be duplicated for classroom or workshop use.

Investigation 1: Grass and Grain Seeds
No. 1—Notebook Master

# Plant Picture

Date _____

Observations _____

_____

_____

_____

_____

FOSS Plants and Animals Module
© The Regents of the University of California
Can be duplicated for classroom or workshop use.

Investigation 1: Grass and Grain Seeds
No. 1—Notebook Master

## Growing and Mowing a Lawn

Cut the six pictures apart.

Put the pictures in order to show what happens when a lawn is planted and grows, is mowed, and then grows again.

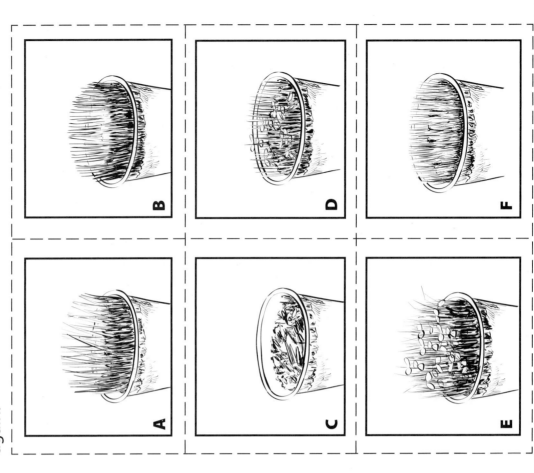

## Growing and Mowing a Lawn

Cut the six pictures apart.

Put the pictures in order to show what happens when a lawn is planted and grows, is mowed, and then grows again.

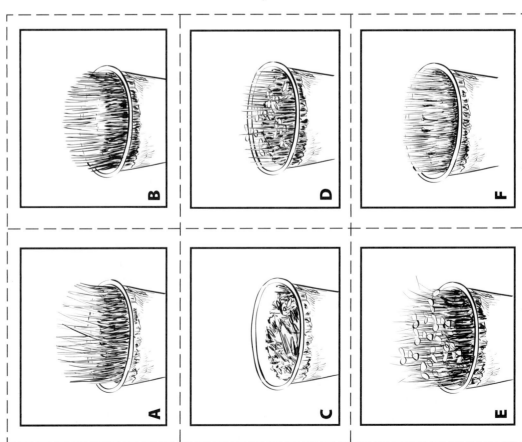

## Growing Wheat

How does a wheat seed grow?

This is the seed.

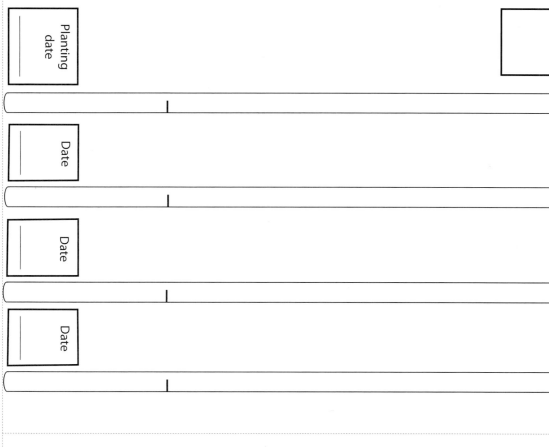

| Planting date ____ | Date ____ | Date ____ | Date ____ |

Investigation 1: Grass and Grain Seeds
No. 3—Notebook Master

---

## Growing Wheat

How does a wheat seed grow?

This is the seed.

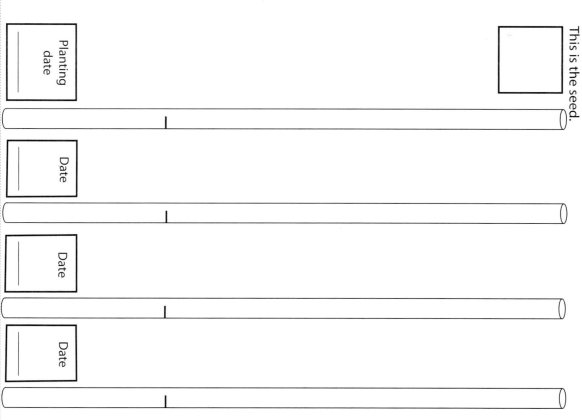

| Planting date ____ | Date ____ | Date ____ | Date ____ |

Investigation 1: Grass and Grain Seeds
No. 3—Notebook Master

## Stem Cuttings

Draw what the cuttings look like after _____ days.

Date _____

Observations _____

_____

_____

## Stem Cuttings

Draw what the cuttings look like after _____ days.

Date _____

Observations _____

_____

_____

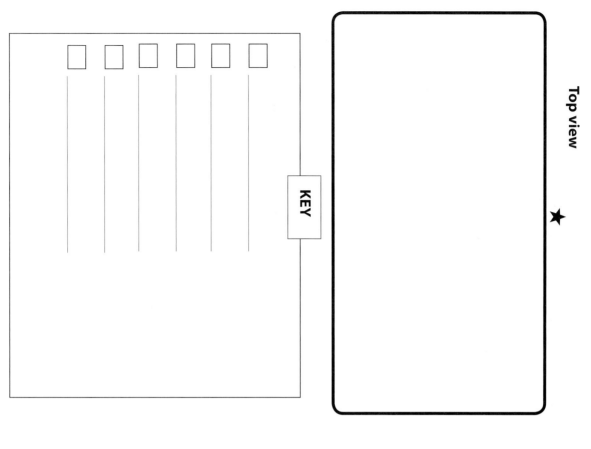

# Terrarium Map

**Top view** ★

**KEY**

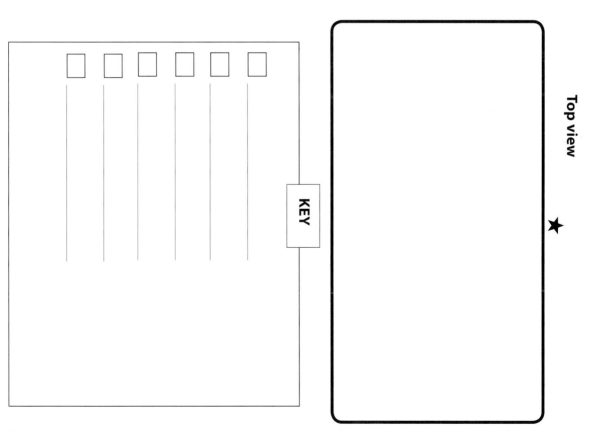

# Terrarium Map

**Top view** ★

**KEY**

## Plants and Animals around the World
### Review Questions

Plants and animals live in many different places called habitats. You read about some of those habitats: rain forest, tundra, desert, forest, grassland, pond, and ocean.

Choose one of these habitats. _____

Tell about a plant and an animal that live in this habitat.

Plant name _____

_____

_____

_____

_____

Animal name _____

_____

_____

_____

_____

---

## Plants and Animals around the World
### Review Questions

Plants and animals live in many different places called habitats. You read about some of those habitats: rain forest, tundra, desert, forest, grassland, pond, and ocean.

Choose one of these habitats. _____

Tell about a plant and an animal that live in this habitat.

Plant name _____

_____

_____

_____

_____

Animal name _____

_____

_____

_____

_____

## Growing Bulbs

### How does a bulb grow?

This is what a bulb looks like before it starts to grow.

| Picture A | Picture B |
|---|---|
| Draw what a bulb looks like when it first starts to grow. | Draw what a bulb looks like 1 week after it starts to grow. |
|  |  |

## Growing Bulbs

### How does a bulb grow?

This is what a bulb looks like before it starts to grow.

| Picture A | Picture B |
|---|---|
| Draw what a bulb looks like when it first starts to grow. | Draw what a bulb looks like 1 week after it starts to grow. |
|  |  |

## Cutting Roots

Cut the radish in three parts.

Plant a piece from each part.

## Cutting Roots

Cut the carrot in four parts.

Plant a piece from each part.

# Teacher Masters

# LETTER TO FAMILY

•••••••••••••••••••••••••••••••••••••••••••••••••••••••

*Cut here and paste onto school letterhead before making copies.*

───────────── ════════════ **SCIENCE NEWS** ═════════ ─────────────

Dear Family,

Our class is beginning a scientific study of plants and animals. We will be investigating several ways to propagate new plants, including growing plants from seed (wheat, oat, ryegrass, and alfalfa, a legume); bulbs (onions and garlic); stems (white potatoes and cuttings from various plants); and roots (carrots and radishes). The scientific thinking processes children will be using in their investigations include observing structures of plants; communicating discoveries orally, in writing, and through drawing; comparing the development of plants over time; and organizing their findings in order to draw conclusions about how different plants reproduce. We will be making a terrarium and comparing the needs of plants and animals. We will be looking at structures of different plants and animals and studying how those features help the plants and animals live in different environments. In addition, we will be going outdoors to investigate the diversity of plants and animals in our schoolyard. I hope you will encourage your child to share his or her growing knowledge of plants and animals at home, and perhaps engage in a few plant-growing activities at home as well.

If your child has specific plant or animal allergies, please let me know so I can plan accordingly.

We will root cuttings in a couple of weeks. If you have one or more plants that you could donate to the science program at that time, I would appreciate it. I could use Swedish ivy, English ivy, coleus, spearmint, or *Tradescantia zebrina* plants.

We're looking forward to lots of fun and lots of learning as we explore a world full of plants and animals! You can get more information on this module by going to www.FOSSweb.com.

Sincerely,

# FOCUS QUESTIONS A

Inv. 1, Part 1: **What happens to ryegrass and alfalfa seeds in moist soil?**

Inv. 1, Part 2: **What happens to the grass and alfalfa plants after we mow them?**

Inv. 1, Part 3: **How does a wheat seed grow?**

Inv. 1, Part 4: **How many different kinds of plants live in an area of the schoolyard?**

Inv. 2, Part 1: **How can we make a new plant from an old one?**

Inv. 2, Part 2: **What grows from the nodes of a potato?**

Inv. 2, Part 3: **How do we keep our cuttings alive?**

# FOCUS QUESTIONS B

Inv. 3, Part 1: **What do plants need to live and grow in a terrarium?**

Inv. 3, Part 2: **What do animals need to live and grow in a terrarium?**

Inv. 3, Part 3: **What structures or behaviors do plants or animals have that help them live in their habitat?**

Inv. 3, Part 4: **How does the behavior of squirrels help them survive the winter?**

Inv. 4, Part 1: **How does a bulb grow?**

Inv. 4, Part 2: **What parts of the plant can grow new plants?**

Inv. 4, Part 3: **How do the plants in the schoolyard compare to the plants studied in class?**

# GROWING A LAWN

_____ | month
_____ | and
_____ | year

| Monday | Tuesday | Wednesday | Thursday | Friday | Sat. | Sun. |
|--------|---------|-----------|----------|--------|------|------|
|        |         |           |          |        |      |      |
|        |         |           |          |        |      |      |
|        |         |           |          |        |      |      |
|        |         |           |          |        |      |      |
|        |         |           |          |        |      |      |

FOSS Plants and Animals Module
© The Regents of the University of California
Can be duplicated for classroom or workshop use.

# WANTED: PLANTS OR STEMS

Dear Family,

We have been growing new plants from seeds. Can we grow new plants from other parts of old plants? Curious scientists want to know!

Our class is in search of whole plants or stems from any of the plants below. Cuttings 25–60 centimeters (cm) (10–24 inches) long, with leaves, would be appreciated.

Please send any stem cuttings in a plastic bag by_____.

Thank you.

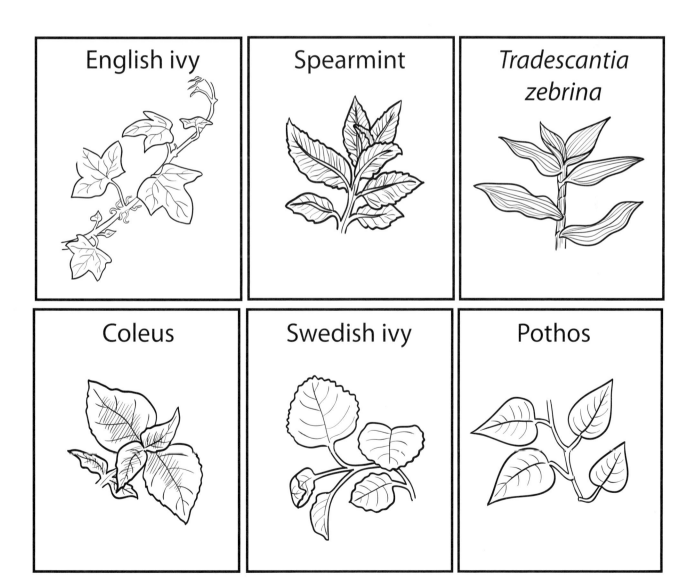

| English ivy | Spearmint | *Tradescantia zebrina* |
| Coleus | Swedish ivy | Pothos |

Name _____ Date _____

# MATH EXTENSION A

· · · · · · · · · · · · · · · · · · · · · · · · · · · · · · · · · · · · · · · · · · ·

## Investigation 1: Grass and Grain Seeds

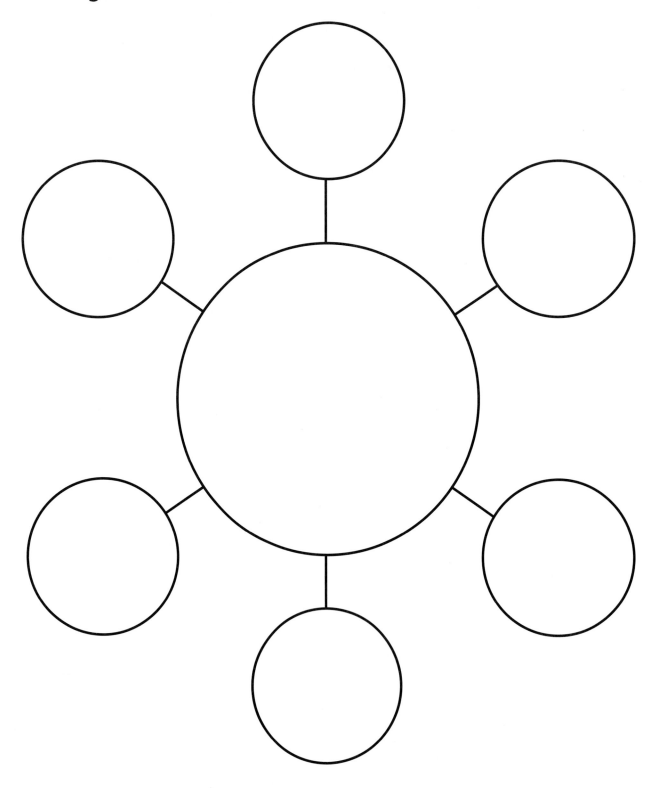

Name _____ Date _____

# MATH EXTENSION B
· · · · · · · · · · · · · · · · · · · · · · · · · · · · · · · · · · · · · ·
## Investigation 1: Grass and Grain Seeds

Many flowers and leaves look the same on
both sides, like this.

1. Color in the half leaf and half flower below.

2. Copy the pattern on the other side to make
   a whole flower or leaf. Color it.

3. Try a three-part
   pattern!

# HOME/SCHOOL CONNECTION

## Investigation 1: Grass and Grain Seeds

Wheat, corn, barley, rice, and oats are grass plants that are staple sources of nutrition for cultures around the world. The abundant seeds of those plants are the group of foods we call grains. You may have examples of grains in your kitchen, perhaps as whole grains of rice or a tortilla made from flour. Here are some places where another grain, corn, might be found in your kitchen.

| | | | | |
|---|---|---|---|---|
| tortillas | cereal | bread | flour | muffins |
| frozen corn | canned corn | popcorn | grits | cornstarch |

Have your child look for examples of grains in your home. He or she can list the examples or bring in a small labeled sample for a class display.

| Wheat | | Corn |
|---|---|---|
| | | |

| Rice | Oats | Barley |
|---|---|---|
| | | |

# MATH EXTENSION A

·  ·  ·  ·  ·  ·  ·  ·  ·  ·  ·  ·  ·  ·  ·  ·  ·  ·  ·  ·  ·  ·  ·  ·  ·  ·  ·  ·  ·  ·  ·  ·  ·  ·  ·  ·  ·  ·  ·  ·

## Investigation 2:  Stems

A girl found a potato.  She saw four nodes on it.  She cut it into four parts and planted it.  She watered it and waited.

Stems and leaves grew from each potato part.  Underground, each potato part grew five new potatoes.

How many new potatoes did the girl grow in all?

# MATH EXTENSION B

· · · · · · · · · · · · · · · · · · · · · · · · · · · · · · · · · · · · · · · · · · · · · · · · · · ·

## Investigation 2:  Stems

Pretend that your class has an old ivy plant that is growing too big.  If every student in your class makes a new plant from an old stem, how many plants would you have?

If your class sells all the new plants for a quarter each, how much money would your class have?

# HOME/SCHOOL CONNECTION

· · · · · · · · · · · · · · · · · · · · · · · · · · · · · · · · · · · · · · · · ·

## Investigation 2: Stems

In class, we are observing how stems grow and sprout. There are many plant stems that we enjoy at our table and see in the market.

Next time you go shopping with your child, please take this checklist and a pencil with you. Ask your child to check off any of the stems that he or she can find. If you find others, write them down.

asparagus

brussels sprouts on a stem

white potato

red potato

broccoli

parsley

celery

artichoke (with stem)

_____

_____

# CENTER INSTRUCTIONS—HABITAT MATCH A

## Materials

Habitat mats

Organism cards for each habitat

## Set up the Center

Select the mats and the cards to be used at the center. Lay the mats out on the center of the table. Keep the cards in separate stacks on top of each mat.

## Guide the Investigation

1. **Introduce the activity.** Show the habitat mats and the eight cards that go with each habitat. Tell students they can do some activities with the mats and cards. They can work in pairs or in groups of three to six. Describe the procedure, modeling the actions as you proceed.

   **Get to know a habitat**

   a. Each person chooses a mat and the matching cards.

   b. Everyone looks at their eight plants and animals on the cards, and sees how they match the habitat.

   c. In turn, each student names their habitat and two things that live there.

   d. Repeat the last step until everyone has had a turn.

   **Habitat match**

   a. Each person chooses a mat and the matching cards.

   b. Take all the cards from students and shuffle them. Each player gets eight new cards, which might not be associated with the habitat on their mat.

   c. In turn, each student calls out two cards. Someone with the matching habitat should say "match" and correctly place it on their mat.

   d. Each person will take turns calling out two cards until all cards have been correctly matched to their habitat.

   **Guess my plant or animal**

   a. Each pair chooses a mat and the matching cards.

   b. The pairs sit side by side with the habitat mat in front of them and the eight cards spread face up around the mat.

   c. One person thinks of one of the cards, but does not tell their partner.

   d. The partner has to ask yes or no questions to guess which plant or animal the person is thinking of.

# CENTER INSTRUCTIONS—HABITAT MATCH B

### Find it

a. Have students pick a new habitat mat. Mix all the cards for those mats and give each student five cards. The rest of the cards go in a stack in the middle of the table.

b. Each student looks for two cards that go with their habitat. If they can, they put the pair on their mat.

c. If they don't have two, they can ask anyone if they have a card that goes with their habitat. If the person has one, they hand it over. Otherwise they say "find it," and the player picks a card from the stack to try to find a pair. They can pick only one card, and then it is the next person's turn.

d. Each person gets a turn, until students find all the cards that match their habitat mat.

### Group the animals and plants

a. Mix the cards for as many habitats as there are students participating.

b. Give each student eight cards.

c. The first person puts one card in the middle of the table.

d. The next person puts down a card that matches the kind of animal it is. For example, if the first card is a hawk, the second person puts down another bird. Other animal groups are reptiles, amphibians, mammals, mollusks, insects, and annelids (earthworms). If it's a plant, then the next card must be a plant.

e. If the next player doesn't have a card that matches, the player puts down a different card.

f. The next person tries to match the first group or the second group.

g. The activity continues, with new groups being established and matches being made, until all the cards are sorted correctly.

2. **Explain and guide the activities.** Depending on the number of students and their interests, suggest different activities. Explain the procedure and help guide the activity. Students might need help reading some of the information on the cards. Some students might want to make up their own activities.

3. **Prepare the center for the next group.** When time is nearly up, ask students to help sort the cards into their habitat groups and place them on top of the appropriate mat for the next group of students.

# MATH EXTENSION A

· · · · · · · · · · · · · · · · · · · · · · · · · · · · · · · · · · · · · · · · · · · · · · ·

## Investigation 3: Terrariums

A girl and a boy each set up a terrarium at home. When the girl counted the plants and animals in her terrarium, the total was 17. When the boy counted the plants and animals in his terrarium, the total was 6 less than the girl's. How many plants and animals did the boy have in his terrarium?

The girl and boy decided to put their plants and animals together in a larger terrarium. How many plants and animals in all will be in this new terrarium?

Name _____ Date _____

# MATH EXTENSION B
· · · · · · · · · · · · · · · · · · · · · · · · · · · · · · · · · · · · · · · · · · · · ·
## Investigation 3: Terrariums

Some students are setting up terrariums in their classroom. They have a total of 20 worms to place in their four terrariums. What are different ways they could put the 20 worms in the terrariums? (The number of worms does not have to be the same in each terrarium.)

# HOME/SCHOOL CONNECTION

## Investigation 3: Terrariums

In class, we have been growing new plants from seeds and from the stems of some plants. By making a simple, low-maintenance terrarium at home, your child can continue to make plant observations. You could plant the terrarium with rooted stem cuttings, seeds, potatoes (a modified underground stem), or yard transplants. Everything the plants need to live is placed inside the terrarium before it is sealed: water, soil, and air. Placed in a well-lit area, out of the sun, the terrarium plants will live untended for a long time.

## Materials

1  2-liter plastic bottle       1   Scissors

•  Soil                         •   Gravel or pebbles

•  Seeds, small plants, or stem cuttings with roots

## Directions

1. Remove the label from a 2-liter plastic bottle. Ask an adult to cut the bottle about 10 centimeters from the bottom. Leave the cap on.

2. Cut four 2.5-centimeter slits along the bottom edge of the top part of the bottle.

3. Put a layer of gravel or small pebbles in the plastic base. Add a layer of soil. If you are planting seeds in the terrarium, fill the soil to near the top edge and plant your seeds.

4. Gently place your rooted cutting in the soil and fill more soil in around it.

5. Water the soil. Place the top section of your bottle on the bottom, fitting the slits over the base.

6. Place the terrarium in a well-lit area. Your terrarium plants have everything they need to live and grow.

Name _____  Date _____

# MATH EXTENSION A
· · · · · · · · · · · · · · · · · · · · · · · · · · · · · · · · · · · · · · · · · · · · · ·
## Investigation 4: Growth and Change

A boy wanted to plant some bulbs in a barrel. He needed to plant them in the fall so they would bloom in the spring.

He went to the nursery and bought five tulip bulbs and six daffodil bulbs. In the spring, all the bulbs grew except for one tulip and one daffodil.

How many bulbs did the boy have blooming in the spring?

Name _____  Date _____

# MATH EXTENSION B

## Investigation 4: Growth and Change

Garlic bulbs grow in a bunch called a head. A head of garlic
can be split into six little bulbs.

Each little bulb can grow into a plant. When the plant is
grown, garlic flowers bloom. Before the plant dies, it makes
a new head with six little bulbs under the ground.

A girl had one head of garlic. She planted each of the bulbs
and soon had flowers blooming in her garden.

She wanted more plants blooming in her garden next year. She dug up the garlic
heads after the plants died, so she could save the bulbs.

How many bulbs do you think she will be able to plant next year?

# HOME/SCHOOL CONNECTION

## Investigation 4: Growth and Change

Read the following story with your child. Then have him or her write an ending to the story, or dictate an ending for you to write.

Once upon a time there lived a poor family who worked hard every day. Papa would go to town and look for jobs. Peter would go to the nearby farms to milk cows, and his mother would mend clothes. Everyone worked hard to put food on the table for the evening meal. Everyone, that is, except Henry. Henry was too young to help Papa with his jobs, too afraid of cows to help his brother, and didn't know how to mend clothes.

One day Henry was sitting by the road to town when a farmer passed on his way to market. "Hello, Henry," called the farmer. "What are you doing sitting alone by the road?"

"Oh, hello," mumbled Henry. "I'm wishing I could help my family. Everyone works so hard so we can buy food for our supper. Everyone but me. I'm too young to help Papa, too afraid of cows to help my brother, and I don't know how to mend clothes with my mother. I'm afraid I'm rather useless."

"Now, Henry," replied the farmer, "no person is useless. We all have ways to help. Sometimes it is difficult to discover how." The farmer reached into his wagon and pulled out a small sack. He handed the sack to Henry and said, "Sometimes all we need is some help getting started and a little creativity. See what you can do with these to help your family. Good luck, Henry." The farmer continued on his way to market.

Henry looked into the sack. He saw a potato, a carrot, and a handful of seeds. "How will one potato, one carrot, and some seeds help me or my family?" Henry wondered. "It's not much of a meal." But as Henry sat and thought, and thought and sat, an idea began to form in his head. As the idea grew, so did his excitement. "I know what I'll do with these!" exclaimed Henry, as he jumped up and ran home.

## What will Henry do?


## How will it help his family?

# Assessment Masters

# Embedded Assessment Notes

Plants and Animals Module

| Investigation ____ , Part ____ | Date_____ |
|---|---|

**Got it!**

**Concept**

**Concept**

**Reflections/Next Steps**

| Investigation ____ , Part ____ | Date_____ |
|---|---|

**Got it!**

**Concept**

**Concept**

**Reflections/Next Steps**

# Scientific Practices Checklist—Plants and Animals Module

Start date _____

End date _____

| Student names | Asking questions and defining problems | Planning and carrying out investigations | Analyzing and interpreting data | Developing and using models | Using mathematics and computational thinking | Constructing explanations and designing solutions | Engaging in argument from evidence | Obtaining, evaluating, and communicating information |
|---|---|---|---|---|---|---|---|---|
| | | | | | | | | |
| | | | | | | | | |
| | | | | | | | | |
| | | | | | | | | |
| | | | | | | | | |
| | | | | | | | | |
| | | | | | | | | |
| | | | | | | | | |
| | | | | | | | | |
| | | | | | | | | |
| | | | | | | | | |
| | | | | | | | | |
| | | | | | | | | |
| | | | | | | | | |
| | | | | | | | | |
| | | | | | | | | |
| | | | | | | | | |
| | | | | | | | | |
| | | | | | | | | |

# Assessment Record

Plants and Animals Module

| Student names | Investigation 1 Benchmark item | | | | Investigation 2 Benchmark item | | | | |
|---|---|---|---|---|---|---|---|---|---|
| | 1 | 2 | 3 | 4 | 1 | 2 | 3 | 4 | 5 |
| | | | | | | | | | |
| | | | | | | | | | |
| | | | | | | | | | |
| | | | | | | | | | |
| | | | | | | | | | |
| | | | | | | | | | |
| | | | | | | | | | |
| | | | | | | | | | |
| | | | | | | | | | |
| | | | | | | | | | |
| | | | | | | | | | |
| | | | | | | | | | |
| | | | | | | | | | |
| | | | | | | | | | |
| | | | | | | | | | |
| | | | | | | | | | |
| | | | | | | | | | |
| | | | | | | | | | |
| | | | | | | | | | |
| | | | | | | | | | |
| | | | | | | | | | |
| | | | | | | | | | |
| | | | | | | | | | |
| | | | | | | | | | |

# Assessment Record

Plants and Animals Module

| Student names | Investigation 3 Benchmark item | | | | Investigation 4 Benchmark item | | | |
|---|---|---|---|---|---|---|---|---|
| | 1 | 2 | 3 | 4 | 1 | 2 | 3 | 4 |
| | | | | | | | | |
| | | | | | | | | |
| | | | | | | | | |
| | | | | | | | | |
| | | | | | | | | |
| | | | | | | | | |
| | | | | | | | | |
| | | | | | | | | |
| | | | | | | | | |
| | | | | | | | | |
| | | | | | | | | |
| | | | | | | | | |
| | | | | | | | | |
| | | | | | | | | |
| | | | | | | | | |
| | | | | | | | | |
| | | | | | | | | |
| | | | | | | | | |
| | | | | | | | | |
| | | | | | | | | |
| | | | | | | | | |
| | | | | | | | | |
| | | | | | | | | |
| | | | | | | | | |
| | | | | | | | | |
| | | | | | | | | |
| | | | | | | | | |
| | | | | | | | | |
| | | | | | | | | |
| | | | | | | | | |
| | | | | | | | | |

# INVESTIGATION 1 I-CHECK
## PLANTS AND ANIMALS

1.  This is a picture of a plant. Use the numbers below to label its parts.

    1 Roots

    2 Stem

    3 Leaves

2.  Circle all the words in the box that tell what a plant needs to grow.

    water              air              space

            rocks              nutrients

    What else do plants need that is not listed in the box?

    _____

3. Write in the missing word for each sentence.

   Word bank:    flowers    roots    seeds    leaves    stems

   _____ take in water and nutrients to help the plant grow.

   _____ make food from sunlight.

4. A boy studied this plant.  He observed that it had seedpods.  He planted the seeds to get more plants.

   Below are three young plants.  Circle the one that grew from a seed from the boy's plant.

**INVESTIGATION 2 I-CHECK**
**PLANTS AND ANIMALS**

Name_____

Date_____

1.  Nodes are places where new plants might grow.  Circle the nodes in the picture.

2.  Match the animals with the ways they help move seeds to new places.

    _____ Bears          A    hide seeds to eat in winter.

                           B    catch seeds on their fur.

    _____ Birds          C    eat seeds, then leave droppings in new
                                places.

    _____ Squirrels

3.  Circle all the words that tell how animals use plants.

         food           shelter          water


              sunlight          air        swimming

4. A girl planted carrot seeds in a garden. When the garden grew, both carrots and weeds were there. How did weeds get into the garden when the girl didn't plant them? Draw or write your ideas.

_____

_____

_____

_____

_____

5. How can we grow new plants? List all the ways you know.

_____

_____

_____

1. Circle the terrarium that matches the map.

   Key

   A  = alfalfa

   G  = grass

    = rocks

2. Circle the word below that is something animals need from their habitats, but plants make for themselves.

   air      water      food      space      light

3.  Match the plant and animals to the places where they live.

| | | | |
|---|---|---|---|
| _____ Cactus | A | Rain forest (very wet) |
| _____ Prairie dog | B | Tundra (very cold) |
| _____ Sloth | C | Desert (very dry) |
| _____ Chipmunk | D | Grassland |
| _____ Caribou | E | Pond |
| _____ Frog | F | Temperate forest |
| _____ Whale | G | Ocean |

4.  Write or draw three ways animal parents take care of their young.

_____

_____

_____

_____

# INVESTIGATION 4 I-CHECK
## PLANTS AND ANIMALS

Name_____

Date_____

1. How can we grow new plants? List all the ways you know.

_____

_____

_____

_____

2. Draw a line with an arrow from each parent animal to the young that it produces.

3.  Write **L** next to the things that are living.  Write **N** next to the things that are not living.

_____ Cactus          _____ Raccoon          _____ Sand

_____ Seed            _____ Water            _____ Tree

_____ Bulb            _____ Rock             _____ Earthworm

4.  Circle all the words in the box that tell what both plants and animals need to live and grow.

| | | |
|---|---|---|
| water | air | space |
| food | shadow | trees |

Which one of the words in the box is something plants can make, but animals must get from their habitat?

_____